DEVON'S HERITAGE

For my grandmother – Marie-Louise

Herbal Folklore

Illustrations by the author

About the Author

Anne-Marie Lafonte wrote "A Herbal Folklore" as a result of spending a year working on the Devon Folklife Register at Rougemont House, Exeter. It began as an interesting project, but rapidly became something much more – and the book will prove a source of unending delight and interest to all those who have never taken Devon's abundant wildlife for granted. Our forbears' homely cures and the uses they made of "herbs and simples" are fascinating, not only as part of our past, but increasingly as a hitherto untapped source of knowledge to help combat present-day ills. No longer are the old-fashioned remedies scoffed at – and many an "old wive's tale" is proving to be unexpectedly beneficial.

Anne-Marie's love affair with Devon began nearly twenty years ago, when she was sent to boarding-school in Exmouth. She firmly resisted the general impetus to move away in search of work, instead sampling a number of local jobs – nurse, librarian, dressmaker, secretary, gardener and museum assistant. She graduated from Exeter University in 1980 with a B.A. (Hons) degree in Theology and is at present researching a Master's degree on the sixteenth century Reformation in Cahors, France.

She writes purely for pleasure, and lives in Budleigh Salterton with her mother three cats and a dog.

SOURCES:

The Devon Folklife Register
The Annual Reports on Devon Folklore – contained within Vols 1-115 of the *Transactions of the Devonshire Association* (1864-1983)
Devon & Cornwall Notes and Queries
Notes and Transcripts from the Ugbrooke Records – transcribed by R.R. Sellman, 1981
Bray, Mrs A.E.: *Traditions of Devonshire,* Vols 1-111, Murray, London, 1900
Northcote, Lady Rosalind: *The Book of Herbs,* John Lane: The Bodley Head
Hewett, Sarah: *Nummits & Crummits,* Thomas Burleigh, London, 1900
Herrick, Robert: *Hesperides, 1648,* Scholar P. 1969
Hole, Mrs: 2 recipe books (Ms) spanning period from 1790-1840 – to be found in the West Country Studies Library.

First published in 1984 by Badger Books, Bideford.
Typeset by Lens Typesetting, Bideford.
Printed in Great Britain by Devon Print Group, Exeter.

Cow Parsnip

It is a constant source of delight to me that wherever I am in Devon, I never have to travel very far to enjoy the richness and beauty of the county's floral heritage. A country walk along any narrow, winding lane uncovers hedgebanks thick with wild flowers – foxgloves and agrimony, primroses, red campion, betony, and many, many more. There are fields carpeted with buttercups and daisies; woodland glades with bluebells and daffodils. Thrift and sea-campion, tree-mallow and the succulent Hottentot fig cling tenaciously to the cliffs; bracken, gorse and ling smother the heaths with their glorious colour. It seems as if the very soil itself cannot contain the wild flowers of Devon, for valerian and pennywort, toadflax, buddleia and heather force themselves through cracks in old walls, and honeysuckle, ivy and brambles ramble over the ruins of ancient buildings and cover tree-stumps. From meadow, hedgerow and garden, from hanging-basket and tub, the sights and scents of flowers feast the senses everywhere.

To the country-folk of Devon's past, however, plants were more than just mere objects to be enjoyed. Of foremost importance was their power to treat and cure both injury and illness, for in isolated communities it was often costly and difficult to obtain medical help. Plants had a whole host of other practical uses, too. When money was short, dandelions, nettles and sorrel provided a free and nutritious source of vegetables; many seeds and flowers could be infused to make refreshing herbal teas, and dandelion-root and goosegrass could both be roasted to yield a pleasant substitute coffee. Plants were found which could be used to make cloth and the substances with which to dye it, and others were effective in washing, starching and even disinfecting clothes and linen. Herbs could be dried, mixed together and either burnt or hung in a room to keep it

sweet-smelling and free from flies, fleas and lice. Large leaves such as those of the butterbur could be wrapped around butter and other foods to keep them fresh, and juniper-berries rubbed over meat kept it free of taint. Heather provided a valuable source of fuel as well as bedding, and broom was excellent for sweeping, as its name suggests. It seems that their purposes were endless.

Those who lived in the rural areas of the county grew to know, love and respect the plants – used here in its widest sense to cover all manner of flowers, shrubs and even trees – that flourished around them. They gave to them affectionate country names which are still used today, and which often give a valuable insight into the beliefs of our Devonian forebears: for example, cuckoo-pints were known as 'adder's meat' because snakes were thought to acquire their poison through eating them; daffodils were 'gooseflops' because their presence was believed to prevent the hatching of geese and other types of poultry; and mountain ash was better known as 'care', because it was held that keeping a stick of it outside the front door would keep witches and other evil spirits at bay. Sometimes the local names express quite simply the medicinal benefits which individual plants were believed to possess; thus, comfrey was widely known as 'knitbone' since it was used to treat sprains and broken bones; coltsfoot was 'coughwort' from its value in treating chest complaints. And while that panacea, valerian, was often referred to simply as 'all-heale',– a colourful Devon name for it is 'bouncing Bess' – it would be nice to think that this name describes the state of rude good health which might follow a valerian cure!

Some of the superstitions attached to the various plants are fascinating, and on occasion very old. Often they can be traced back to ancient religious beliefs or customs: for instance, far back in history parsley used to be placed on the forehead of a person who had died, and also strewn onto the grave, so the association with death lingers still. The belief that elder should never be taken indoors or burnt can be traced back to the conviction that it was this tree which provided the wood for the crucifixion, and since hawthorn and blackthorn have both been accused of being used to fashion Christ's crown of thorns, each has sinister connotations. Equally interesting is the way in which herbs that originally had an important part to play in pagan ritual have subsequently become linked with Christianity: perhaps the Church recognised that superstitions held by inhabitants of remote rural communities were too deeply-rooted to be destroyed, and so absorbed them instead into Christian legend. Vervain is just one example: its reputation dates back to Roman times at least, for the Romans believed that it possessed the power to heal all injuries valorously and honourably acquired, and to confer immortality upon heroes: it is not surprising, therefore, to learn that it was also thought to have been used to treat the wounds of Christianity's immortal saviour, Jesus Christ.

Such beliefs, which might originally have come to Devon from other parts of the country, or even other parts of the world, have been passed down from family to family and generation to generation, being gradually moulded, embroidered and added to, until eventually they have acquired a character all their own. Where but in Devon, for example, is there such a rich store of superstition concerning the ash tree? Lovers considered it an aphrodisiac; young girls divined their future husbands by it; it could be a harbinger of good luck, or an indicator of the weather ahead; local charmers used it to kill snakes, cure snake-bite, cause warts to disappear, and heal ruptures in children; then at Christmas it was made into a faggot and burnt in commemoration of the fire it was thought to have furnished in the stable at Bethlehem. Lit through the festive season, it kept evil spirits at bay and provided entertainment for the friends and families who gathered around it; children showed their courage by it, and men their virility; young girls yearned to learn from it whom they would marry.

Superstitions and customs such as these are part of the rich and absorbing folklore of our county, but while there are still old folk who remember a time when the Ashen Faggot was burnt at Christmastide, or can recall decorating a 'kissing-bush' made from furze and other evergreen foliage to take the place of a Christmas tree, except in a very few instances such customs remain only as a memory, a memory which I hope this book will help to keep alive.

Although I think I must have inherited my love of flowers and fascination for the superstitions and legends which surround them from my grandmother, my interest increased enormously during the year I was privileged to spend working on the Devon Folklife Register. Housed at Rougemont House Museum in Exeter, the Register collects and stores material on the social and cultural history of the County, and cannot fail to absorb anyone with a feel for Devon folklore. Local people, too, were most helpful and generous in coming forward by telephone, letter, or indeed in person with remembered cures or curiosities: to them, and to the Register, I am profoundly grateful.

Although he will never know it, I am grateful also to Robert Herrick, the seventeenth century Devon poet who spent much of his life as vicar of Dean Prior. In his famous collection of poems, the 'Hesperides', Herrick drew often upon flowers for his imagery: he had the sensitivity to see the transience of life reflected in a rose or a daffodil, and the bitter-sweetness of love in myrtle or primroses. He wrote of old Devon games, such as burning the Ashen Faggot. His poetry is at times amusing, sensual, moving, reflective, and always perceptive, and I have taken the liberty of quoting freely from it in the pages which follow. And in the hope that the flowers of Devon's countryside, and the legends and superstitions associated with them, may never be allowed to die out, I steal these lines which Herrick originally dedicated 'To his booke', that they may equally apply to Devon's herbal lore:-

'Thou art a plant, sprung up to wither never,
But like a laurel, to grow green for ever.'

AGRIMONY *(Agrimonia eupatoria)*

- Aaron's Rod
- Church Steeples
- Fairy's Rod
- Fairy's Wand

Agrimony is a flower of hedgerows and roadside verges, with small yellow flowers borne on slender spikes. The fruits – known popularly as 'clitch-button' or 'sticky-button' – are topped by a ring of hooks which catch on fur and clothing, so widespread distribution is assured.

The local names for this plant provide good examples of the Church's desire to supersede beliefs which, at their heart, were obviously pagan. Early in history, agrimony had been associated with magic, so it was frequently known in Devon as 'Fairy's Wand' or 'Fairy's Rod'. These names, however, were unacceptable to sober-minded Christians, so the variation 'Aaron's Rod' was introduced, and it was probably at this time that the plant also became known as 'Church Steeples'.

Agrimony has traditionally been used as a dye in rural areas, the colour produced depending on the time of year that the flower was gathered: flowers picked in late summer yield a pale yellow dye, deepening as the plant matures towards the end of Autumn.

The plant was also one of our earliest air-fresheners, for even when dry its apricot scent continues to perfume the atmosphere; hence sprays were hung indoors to keep the house smelling sweet.

Medicinally, agrimony was used in North Devon in the last century for consumptive patients: it was infused with equal quantities of raspberry-leaves and barberry-bark.

It is still used today as a tonic, for it acts upon the nervous system, counteracting fatigue and relieving stress; in addition, it benefits those troubled by bladder problems or stomach pains. The tonic is made by steeping an ounce of dried agrimony in a pint of boiling water: this should be done in a covered pot, and the mixture allowed to stand till cold. It may then be strained and sweetened, and half a teacupful taken three times a day. As well as being highly beneficial to the kidneys, the same infusion is said to be an effective means of curing a sore throat.

Sufferers from insomnia might care to try sleeping on a pillow which has agrimony included in its filling, for an old rhyme asserts that:-

'If you lay Agrimony under your head
You shall sleep as if you were dead;
You shall never dread nor waken
Till from under your head it be taken.'

The plant also has its uses in the field of veterinary medicine, for sheep and goats are very fond of it, and it has been found to relieve jaundice in animals, and to stop bleeding and heal sprains.

Finally another of agrimony's virtues emerges from the seventeenth century records of Ugbrooke House, near Chudleigh, for it was one of the principal ingredients in a recipe for Usquebaugh – better known today as Whisky!

APPLES

To think of apples in Devon is to think of cider, for the cider industry is one of the oldest in the region. Being of vital importance to the economy of the county, it was essential that all possible means should be taken to ensure a healthy yield of apples, hence the annual custom of Wassailing. This took place either on Old or New Christmas Eve or New Year's Eve, and took the form of a traditional ceremony designed to appease the spirit of the apple tree: it was hoped that the spirit would duly repay the devotion of those taking part by producing a bumper crop of apples in the season to come. Locals would gather in the orchard around the heaviest cropping tree and chant one of a number of rhymes, such as:

'Here's to thee, old apple tree,
Whence thou may'st bud, and when thou may'st blow!
And whence thou may'st bear apples enow!
Hats full! Caps full!
Bushel – bushel – sacks full!
And my pockets full too, Hurra!'

They would then take a liberal supply of cider – often containing toast, wheat-flour cakes or roasted apples – and anoint the roots, trunks and branches of the trees for it was thought that:

'More or less fruit they will bring
As you do give them wassailing'.

In some places the cider-soaked toast or cakes were placed in a fork in the tree; in others it was pelted with apples, but in each case the purpose was the same – to charm the apple-tree spirit. On the other hand, harmful spirits had to be chased away: the assembled company therefore made as much noise as possible by shouting and screaming, banging on metal objects such as pots and pans, and firing guns into the branches of the trees. Such intimidating behaviour was designed to ensure that no evil would dare come near them.

Nevertheless, Devonians believed that despite their best endeavours, the apple crop remained in danger during three particular nights in May, known as Franklin Nights or Francimass. Apparently, the nights of the 17th, 18th and 19th of the month (or in some versions of the legend the 19th, 20th and 21st) are always cold and frosty, so that the blossom is put at grave risk. One explanation of the phenomenon comes from the Taw Valley, and tells of a brewer named Frankan who was worried at the effect which the local preference for cider was having upon his sale of ale: hence, he sold his soul to the Devil on condition that the latter would send three frosty nights each May to destroy the apple blossom.

Another version of the story maintains that the brewers of North Devon vowed that they would put some noxious substance into their ale if Satan would help them by killing the budding fruit. Accordingly, whenever these frosts came it was maintained that the Devil had fulfilled his part of the bargain, and that the brewers had duly kept theirs by adulterating the beer! Hence, in North Devon the Devil is sometimes nick-named 'St Franklin'.

A slightly older version of the legend from the south of the county associated these nights with St Dunstan, claiming that this saint once bought up a quantity of barley and made it into beer. The Devil, knowing that Dunstan would naturally wish to get a good price for this brew, offered, in exchange for his soul, to blight the apple-trees so that there would be no cider, and hence an increased demand for ale. The saint agreed, but stipulated that the trees should be blighted on three specific nights, ending with his own feast day on 19th May.

Another tale related that on this night in May three powerful witches pass through the air; if they drop charms on the blossoming orchards the crops are spoiled.

All these superstitions reveal the importance given to apples in Devon, an importance highlighted by this little local rhyme extolling their medicinal benefits:

'Eat an apple going to bed,
Make a doctor beg his bread.'

They could be used, too, to charm away warts. To this end, it was necessary to cut an apple in half and rub each section over the warts: the two halves were then tied together and buried, on the principle that as they rotted, the wart would rot away with them. Alternatively, one half could be rubbed over the blemish and then given to a pig to eat, and the other half eaten by the sufferer himself: this was thought to be equally effective.

ASH *(Fraxinus excelsior)*

– Keys of heaven (seeds)

Unlike other trees, Ash has the property of burning while still green, supposedly because on the night that Our Saviour was born, it was collected to make a fire in the stable at Bethlehem. Beside it Jesus was said to have received his first bath, so in times past in Devon new-born babies were also traditionally bathed for the first time beside a fire made from ash.

Devonians also believed that it was in the light of this fire that Christ was dressed in swaddling bands, and this event has been commemorated in the county by a custom which still prevails in certain areas, the burning of the Ashen Faggot or Facket. This was lit on Christmas Eve, and consisted of green ash-sticks, bound or 'swaddled' with twisted hazel or ash binders or 'beens'; the whole was then held together by chains. The size of the faggots varied according to the size of the fireplace in which they were to be burnt, but in some instances they were large enough to keep smouldering throughout the entire twelve days of Christmas. Whilst alight, evil spirits were supposedly kept at bay.

On Christmas Eve friends would gather round an open fire and the log would be set alight, often using a piece of the previous year's faggot. As each 'been' burst a loud 'snap' would be heard and punch or cider circulated around the assembled group amid loud cheers. Some particular local customs were associated with the procedure: in Ashburton the youngest child of the household used to be placed upon the faggot as the wood started to crackle, in the belief that the length of time that the child stayed there would be a measure of its future courage or timidity. And in similar fashion, once the log had burnt enough to make the chains unnecessary the men would be anxious to demonstrate their manliness by removing them, still very hot, with their bare hands. In some areas young girls would use the faggot to learn when they would be married: each girl present would select a band; the owner of the first band to burst would be the first to marry.

The custom of the Ashen Faggot is an ancient one: the Devon poet, Robert Herrick, knew of a similar practice, as his poem 'Ceremonies for Christmasse' recounts:-

'Come, bring with a noise,
My merrie, merrie boys,
The Christmas Log to the firing;
While my good Dame, she
Bids ye all be free;
And drink to your hearts desiring.

With the last year's brand
Light the new block, and
For good success in his spending,
On your psaltries play,
That sweet luck may
Come while the Log is a teending.'

In Herrick's day it was obviously the custom to re-light the Log on the final day of Christmas – Candlemas Eve – and allow it to burn until sunset. It was then dismantled, with only a small part being kept to light the following year's brand. In these lines he gives the reason for this:

'Kindle the Christmas brand and then
Till sunne-set let it burne;
Which quencht, then lay it up agen
Till Christmas next returne.

Part must be kept wherewith to teend
The Christmas Log next yeare;
And where 'tis safely kept; the Fiend
Can do no mischiefe there.'

The association between the ash tree and the Nativity may account for the peculiar power which it is said to possess over snakes, since in Biblical tradition snakes are often associated with Satan. The leaves of the tree have long figured in Devonian charms against the bites of vipers, and it is said that if one traces a circle around a sleeping viper with an ash stick, then the snake is sure to die.

Local healers believed ash to be effective in

a number of charms. For instance to be rid of warts within three days the sap was gathered from a burning green stick and rubbed on the warts while still hot, according to a Hartland charm from the 1920s. A hundred years ago a child suffering from a rupture might have been subjected to the following curious ritual: a little boy from Honiton was taken by his mother and her two daughters to a neighbouring wood, where the daughters selected an ash sapling and split it down the centre. Standing one on each side of the split, they passed their brother between it three times, and then bound the two halves together. The idea was that as the two halves of the tree knitted together, the child would be healed. A male child required two females to carry out the procedure, and a female child two males; the parent would play no part. The 'Ash-Tree Cure' was also known at Kingswear, and in the 1870s in a wood at Spitchwich near Ashburton it was noticed that a number of ash trees had evidently been used for this purpose: a local resident was able to instance several young men in the neighbourhood who had been subjected to this treatment and had subsequently grown up strong and healthy. On the other hand, one lad whose tree had not knitted had remained sickly and deformed.

Country-folk observe ash and oak trees in the Spring to see which will come into leaf the first, for from this they believe that they can foretell whether the season will be a wet one or not, for:

'If the Oak before the Ash, then we shall have a splash;
If the Ash before the Oak, then we shall have a soak.'

Unusually-shaped ash leaves are believed to have their own special significance: the finding of a double- leaved ash is a sign that great good luck is on its way, whilst an even-leaved ash promises that one's true love will appear before the day is over. A woman finding such a leaf should hold it flat between both hands, repeating softly:

'With this even-leafed ash between my hands
The first I meet will be my dear man.'

She should then place it in the palm of the gloved right hand and say:

'This placed in my glove
Will bring my own true love.'

Then press it against her bosom and whisper:

'This even-leafed ash in my bosom
Will give me, in the first man I meet,
My true husband.'

And lovers may be interested to know that according to country superstition ash seeds are an effective aphrodisiac!

ASPEN *(Populus tremula)*

– Pipple
– Pippler

It takes only the slightest breeze to set the leaves of the Aspen a-quiver. An old superstition, widespread throughout Devon, claims that this is because it was Aspen wood which was used to make the Holy Cross. The tree now trembles in shame and horror at the thought of the part which it had to play in Christ's crucifixion.

According to the ancient 'Doctrine of Signatures' which asserted that trees and herbs give some outward sign of the purpose for which they were intended, the shivering leaves of the aspen were thought to indicate that the tree could be used to treat ague.

BALM *(Melissa officinalis)*

Lemon balm, so called because of its pleasant lemony aroma when crushed, is a herb which is similar in appearance to mint.

The official name for this plant – 'Melissa' – is derived from the Greek word for a bee, and bees are certainly greatly attracted to it. Beekeepers used to rub their hives with balm both to prevent the bees from straying and to cause other bees to join them. The honey produced from this plant was very highly esteemed.

Because of its fresh, lemon scent, balm was one of the old-fashioned 'strewing-herbs' – plants scattered throughout the house to sweeten and purify the air. It was, and still is, included in mixtures for pot pourris.

The herb is a useful one medicinally: lemon balm tea is considered soothing in a number of conditions, ranging from feverishness (it induces copious perspiration), catarrh, headaches, earache or toothache, to stomach upsets such as indigestion, nausea and flatulence. To make the tea the herb should be cut just as it comes into flower and dried in a warm, shady place: when brittle, the leaves can be rubbed from the stalks and stored in an airtight container to be used when required. An ounce is infused in a pint of boiling water, and a wineglassful of the tea drunk several times a day.

Crushed balm leaves mixed with salt make an excellent emergency treatment for wounds and sores, having a cleansing as well as a soothing effect.

BAY *(Laurus nobilis)*

– Laurel

Slow-growing, evergreen and aromatic, the Bay-tree was once regarded as a symbol of the continuance of life, steadfast and enduring. In past times it was one of the chief funeral herbs, often being combined with rosemary. Robert Herrick wrote of it as the ideal epitaph, in the "Hesperides":

'A funeral stone
Or verse I covet none;
But only crave
Of you, that I may have
A sacred Laurel springing from my grave:
Which being seen
Blest with perpetual green,
May grow to be
Not so much call'd a tree,
As the eternal monument of me.'

Bay trees did occasionally wither, however, and when this happened it was taken to be an extremely evil omen, usually portending death. The superstition was widespread, and although known in Devon it was not confined to the county, for Shakespeare recorded it in these lines from Richard II:

'Tis thought the King is dead; we will not stay.
The Bay-trees in our country are all wither'd...'

Laurel had happier associations too, for again, with rosemary, it was a traditional decoration both at weddings and Christmas. Perhaps its most famous use was in the making of the Laurel Wreath. This was a garland made up of Bay leaves and awarded most often for literary excellence, although achievement in other spheres was also recognised in this way: for example, victors in the Olympic Games were traditionally crowned with Laurel wreathes. It was a custom again mentioned by Robert Herrick, in a poem dedicated to Ben Johnson:

'Thou had'st the wreath before, now take the Tree.
That henceforth none be Laurel crowned but thee.'

William Browne, another of our Devon poets, also spoke of this wreath in his "Britannia Pastorales":

'Where Bayes still grow (by thunder not struck down)
The victor's garland and the poet's crown.'

And in doing so referred to another old belief concerning the Bay-tree; namely, that neither thunder nor lightning have any power to harm it. The reason which Browne gives for this is that 'being the materials of poets' ghirlands, it is supposed not subject to any of Jupiter's thunderbolts, as other trees are.'

The country-folk of Devon used to believe that many types of birds, among them stock-doves, jays, merles, blackbirds and certain thrushes, ate bay to recover their lost appetites.

BEANS

Throughout the County, advice may be found concerning the planting of beans – be they runner, kidney or broad. The residents of George Nympton traditionally waited to plant their runner beans until after their annual revel, held on a Wednesday near to St. Georges's Day (23rd April). Presumably it was supposed that beans planted at a festival associated with their patron saint would enjoy his protection. Practically, it was a suitable time for sowing the vegetable, for the worst of the frosts would be over by then. Similarly, gardeners in Sampford Peverell believed in waiting until Sampford Fair before planting theirs, whereas the folk of Culmstock preferred a date exactly a week later than this, namely the first Monday in May. On this day they too held a fair, and the beans were supposed to be planted while this was actually in process; a local maxim claimed that 'before you go is too early; after you've come back is too late!'

No specific date was prescribed in the case of kidney-beans; in this instance one should instead be regulated by the growth-rate of elm leaves, as this verse advises:

'When elm leaves are as big as a shilling
Plant kidney-beans if to plant them you are willing;
When elm leaves are a big as a penny
You must plant kidney-beans if you mean to have any.'

As with all beans, they would do much better if sown on a waxing moon.

An old Squire of Broadclyst was convinced that French beans should be planted as soon as the first cuckoo was heard. Indeed, so firmly did he hold this belief that he would accost any tenants that he met and urge them to hie home at once and sow their seeds!

Good Friday was another good time for planting beans. F.J. Snell, in his 'Book of Exmoor', tells of a new minister who was much perturbed at the poor attendance at his Good Friday service. On remarking upon the fact, he was told that his congregation were busy sowing their beans so that the young seedlings might make their appearance on Easter Sunday.

How the plants grew was also significant. At the beginning of the century the people of South Molton believed that if a scarlet runner-bean plant came up with white leaves, a death would shortly occur.

Beans feature in certain local charms and cures. A Hartland charm for warts from the 1920s advised that a broad bean should be picked and shelled, and the inner part rubbed over the warts. The pod should be buried, so that as it rotted, the wart disappeared. An Exeter resident, who tried the charm on a wart which she had on her leg in 1982, is able to testify to the efficacy of the cure, although a similar charm from Culmstock specifies that the treatment will only work if the broad bean is a stolen one.

The furry interior of the pod is also soothing if applied to chapped lips, and an East Devon lady recommends that in severe cases the pod should be kept on the lips overnight. The same bean-pod is also said to relieve nettle stings.

BETONY

(Betonica (Stachys) officinalis)

Betony was once one of our most used herbs, but it has now lost its place in many herb gardens, and survives only in some old churchyards and cottage gardens, in meadows, and along woodland paths.

In former times betony was thought to be a powerful protection against the forces of evil, and so was traditionally planted in all churchyards to protect the spirits of the departed. This is probably why it was also deemed to have control over snakes, for in Christian mythology the serpent has always been associated with Satan. It was believed that if a ring of Betony was placed upon the ground, snakes placed within it would fight to the death.

Although it has fallen out of favour as a medicinal herb, it was once so highly esteemed by herbalists that their advice was to 'sell your coat and buy betony'. It was used for disorders of the brain, as a purgative or, in cases of poisoning, an emetic.

Betony was one of the ingredients in a seventeenth century cure for 'Spitting of Blood', practised at Ugbrooke House, near Chudleigh. The recipe required that one should boil betony, marsh-mint and rue in goats's milk, and drink the brew for four days.

The herb could be used, too, in the treatment of animals. It was boiled in either ale or vinegar and given to horses suffering from toothache.

BILBERRY *(Vaccinium myrtillus)*

– Hurtleberry
– Whortleberry

Autumn visitors to Dartmoor will be familiar with the bilberry, for it grows happily on poor, acid soils and so abounds upon the Moor.

The fruits of the bilberry are rich in both flavour and goodness: they are a very good source of Vitamins C and D and were much valued as a dye. Over the years it has become traditional for whole families to make for the Moor for the annual 'Urting' or 'whorting' expedition, with children often being excused school for the day. A certain amount of ritual accompanied the gathering of the bilberries, for it was believed that for best results, the pickers should recite together the following charm:

'The first I pick, I eat
The second I pick, I throw away;
The third I pick, I put in my can.'

In Ashburton in Victorian times it was customary for the Board School to be closed for a week so that the pupils could harvest the crop. The first crop came in Awsewell or 'Azel' Wood and children would spend entire days picking. Sometimes, on the way home, a party of Buckfastleigh boys might be encountered; this often led to fighting during which baskets might be overturned!

The day's pickings were measured (not weighed) and payment made at 3d or 4d a quart. An average day's picking would be a quart or three pints per child.

BINDWEED, GREATER

(Convolvulus (Calystegia) sepium)

- Bryony
- Charliepots (Whimple)
- Convovulus
- Grandma's Nightcap (Stockland)
- Ground Ivy
- Honeysuckle
- Lady's Smock
- London Bells
- Morning Glory
- Old Woman's Bonnet
- Wandering Willie
- Withywind

Although to gardeners the name 'bindweed' will immediately conjure visions of a most troublesome weed, to the unjaundiced eye the sight of hedges, wasteland and banks covered with large, handsome, funnel-shaped white or pale-pink flowers is one to be enjoyed.

These flowers warn us when rain is on its way by closing tightly to protect the rich store of nectar contained within. They close, too, when picked, although country folk have found a means of 'tricking' them; the entire trailing stem is plunged into water before being cut so that no air is able to enter into it. If the cut end is then kept in water the flowers will remain open for several days.

The greater bindweed is unusual in that it keeps its blossoms open well into the night if the weather is fine. If the moon is bright they may not close at all, so that when the sun rises the trumpet-shaped flowers will be open to greet it. This characteristic has led to the plant being known locally as 'Grandma's Nightcap' and 'Morning Glory'.

BLACKBERRY *(Rubus fruticosus)*

– Brambles
– Brimbles
– Brimmles

There can be few Devonians who have never raided the hedgerows for the delicious fruits of the blackberry, and sayings about blackberry time figure frequently in Devonian folklore. An ancient Bideford superstition warns that they should never be gathered after 20th September, for on that day the Devil is said to leave his mark upon them and anyone who picks the fruit after this date will fall into his hands.

In the Exeter area it was considered unlucky to eat blackberries after Michaelmas Day for the same reason, whereas in South Molton it was on 10th October (old Michaelmas Eve), that Satan was thought to spit upon the fruit. In somewhat coarser vein, the residents of Bampton would never pick the berries after Bampton Fair ''cos that's when the Devil 'ave widdled on 'em'! Since this fair was held on the last Thursday in October, the blackberry obviously enjoyed an unusually long season in that area.

The origin of these superstitions dates back to an old legend which states that Satan, cast out of heaven, came to earth upon a bramble bush. In fury, he cursed the plant and each year, on the anniversary of his downfall, is said to spoil the crops by spitting (or worse!) upon them. Anyone picking the fruit after this blighting is sure to have bad luck.

The people of Barnstaple also have a legend which associates blackberries with the Devil. They say that when Barnstaple Fair was held on the feast of St. Michael, Old Nick decided to pay it a visit and whilst there feasted upon some blackberries. Finding them delicious, and being naturally greedy, he overate of them, became ill and died!

Delicious as the fruit is, the passing of the blackberry-season was not mourned by everyone, for while it lasted illness among animals and humans seemed to increase. Thus, from Hennock comes the remark 'Baby's not well, it's blackberry time'. And amongst the animals whose health is thought to suffer at this time are horses (Chudleigh Knighton), cats (Cruwys Morchard) and even chickens. The fishermen of the county, however, awaited blackberry-time with interest, for local superstition maintains that if it is a good season for blackberries, it will also be a good season for herring.

An unusual purpose to which brambles have been put in Devon is the catching of rabbits: a 'brimble' was stripped of all its 'preckles' (thorns) except for about 3–4 inches at the tip. It was then fed down the rabbit-hole with a twisting movement which would ensure that it penetrated as far as possible. When it would go no further it was given a few extra twists so that if it had come to rest against a rabbit the 'preckles' would become entangled in the animal's fur and it could be pulled out into the open.

Brambles also served as a reasonable substitute for twine, and were particularly employed in broom and basket making; and an orange-yellow dye from the roots was often used to colour wool and cloth.

The blackberry bush figures in a number of curious Devonian charms. Only 30 years ago a child with sore eyes was taken to a doctor in North Tawton, who noticed that the child's body was badly scratched and demanded an explanation. 'Well' replied the mother, 'Us tried to cure 'un. Us drawed 'un three times through a brimble-bush backwards, and us got the old duck to quack three times into the mouth of 'un, but that didn't cure 'un, so us brought 'un to 'ee.'

A similar charm was used to treat boils, known locally as 'pinzoles', 'pinzels' or 'blackheads'. In Rockbeare, in the 1870s, the sufferer was required to creep underneath an arched bramble – i.e. one growing into the ground at both ends. Thirty years later, in Great Torrington, the procedure was rather more complicated: here the afflicted person was to go fasting to such a bramble for three Sunday mornings in succession, and to crawl under it 'the way of the sun', probably three times. The boils would then vanish. The charm was supposed to be specially effective if the two ends of the arched bramble grew in different properties.

A Hartland charm for warts, dating from the 1920s, also involved the use of blackberries. One was instructed to pick the first blackberry one saw, rub it on the wart, and throw it away. The idea was that as the berry decayed, the wart would vanish.

Blackberries also had medicinal uses. In Tiverton, in the 1930s, the leaves were used to treat 'scanter' (dysentery). A double handful of blackberry leaves was steeped in water and the resultant brew given to the patient to drink. The same treatment is still recommended for diarrhoea, especially in children.

The berries, too, have been found to be useful bowel regulators, for when ripe they have a laxative effect, and when green will combat diarrhoea instead. Over-ripe blackberries are indigestible, however, hence the local superstitious warning against eating them too late in the season.

Today, blackberry leaves are used locally as a tonic or to comfort sufferers from shingles. An ounce of clean, healthy leaves should be infused in a pint of boiling water, strained and bottled, and a wineglassful taken night and morning.

For those afflicted with a sore throat and hoarse voice, a spoonful of blackberry jam, mixed in a cup of hot water, will produce a soothing and beneficial drink.

BLACKTHORN

(Prunus spinosa)

- Castings
- Gawks
- Gribble
- Grig
- Sloe
- Slone/sloan

The blackthorn has been treated with some suspicion in Devon. In the 1920s the people of Hartland were decidedly wary of bringing it into the house, for they believed that great bad luck would follow. Neither did they like to see a blackthorn tree heavily laden with fruit, for to them 'many sloans' (sloes) heralded 'many groans' (much sickness). This suspicion may perhaps be traced back to an old belief that blackthorn had been used to fashion Christ's crown of thorns.

Around the 1870s, a resident of Chudleigh who suffered from boils might have been sent early in the morning, while the dew was still on the grass, to a thorn bush and told to crawl round it backwards three times. The boils were then supposed to disappear.

Medicinally, blackthorn bark was an ancient remedy for bronchitis. The bark was boiled in a saucepan of water, then allowed to cool, the mixture sweetened and drunk whenever necessary.

It is from the fruits of the blackthorn that sloe gin is made. The tough skin of the sloe becomes softened and more absorbent after frost so the fruit is best picked just after the first frost of the autumn, and in order that maximum flavour may be imparted to the gin it is best if each sloe is pierced with a sharp knife. Equal weights of fruit and sugar should be put into bottles, so that the bottles are half filled; these should then be topped up with gin, leaving just a little space at the neck, and the bottles tightly stoppered. The mixture needs to be stored for several months, being shaken slightly from time to time to ensure thorough mixing of the ingredients. Sloe gin makes a delicious liqueur to have at Christmas.

BLUEBELL

(Campanula rotundifolia)

- Blue Goocools (Kingsbridge)
- Cross-Flower
- Cuckoo-Flower
- Goosey-Gander (Moretonhampstead)
- Gramfer-Greg (Moretonhampstead)

Bluebells are aptly named, for their delicate bell-shaped flowers are indeed a rich shade of blue, although white or pale pink varieties can be found. The fragrant flowers appear between April and June and clothe the hedgerows, woods, and clifftops of the county. Their numbers have unfortunately declined in recent years, partly through being over picked – bluebells reproduce from seed rather than from bulb offsets – but even more so through being trampled upon, for recent research has shown that if the leaves are crushed, the plant will die from lack of food. As a preservation measure, it has now been made illegal to uproot the bulbs of bluebells growing in the wild.

Devon superstition maintains that this is one of the flowers which it is unlucky to bring into the house of anyone who keeps poultry. As with daffodils and primroses, the reason seems to be that such an action will adversely affect the hatching of any goslings, ducklings or chicks.

When cut, bluebells yield a sticky substance which was used as an early form of glue. Glue could also be obtained from the bulb, as could a starch which was widely used in the days when fashion decreed that collars and ruffs should be crisply stiffened. Like that of arum, however, bluebell starch was highly irritant and caused painful sores on the hands of the unfortunate laundresses.

BROOM

(Cytisus (Sarothamnus) scoparius)

– Green Broom
– Little Fair-One (Hawkchurch)
– Wood-Wax

Broom flourishes on heaths, sandy areas and open woods throughout the county, growing to some 2m in height. Its attractive, golden-yellow flowers, which are similar in shape to those of the sweet-pea, appear between May and June, and are followed by long, bean-shaped pods. Unlike the gorse, it has no spines, bearing instead small leaves like those of the trefoil.

In medieval times the broom was officially known as 'Planta Genista', and when Henry II maintained family tradition by taking the flower as his emblem he adopted also its name – 'Plantagenet' – for his Royal House. A broom plant with open empty pods appears on the tomb of Richard II in Westminster Abbey.

As its name suggests, broom was traditionally used for making brushes, especially of the type that witches were supposed to ride upon by night. However, a common superstition warns that anyone who sweeps the floor with blossomed broom in May is surely sweeping one of the household away. Devon housewives were wary even of using broom for indoor decoration during this month, lest they might be putting one of the family at risk. This wariness did not extend to other months of the year, however, for in past times broom was used to deck the Church for a Spring wedding.

Arable farmers in the county are still pleased to see a Broom plant heavily laden with blossom, for they believe that this indicates that the coming harvest will be a plentiful one.

The medicinal uses of the plant have long been recognised: in Chudleigh, in the seventeenth century, it was used to treat dropsy: enough was burnt to produce half a pint of ashes, and these were steeped in old mountain wine for a fortnight. A beer glass of this was then taken night and morning.

Green broom was also used to cure jaundice: it was boiled until very bitter in posset (hot milk, curdled by the addition of wine, ale or vinegar, and usually spiced); half a pint of this was drunk every morning before food for a week.

Broom is a dangerous plant to experiment with unwarily: several varieties of it occur, and some, like the Spanish Broom (Spartium junceum) which is a common garden plant, are poisonous. Even the wild broom mentioned above should be treated with respect, for it has narcotic properties which become evident when one observes the drugged behaviour of sheep feeding upon it.

BUTCHERS' BROOM

(Ruscus aculeatus)

– 'Knee-Holly'

The pale green and violet flowers of the Butchers' Broom appear between January and April, often alongside bright red fruits from the previous year. Both male and female flowers may be found on the same plant, occurring in the centre of what appears to be a leaf, but is actually a stiff, sharp, dark-green stem which fulfils the energy-producing function of a leaf, and gives the shrub the appearance of an evergreen. Butchers' Broom favours a fairly dry habitat, and may often be found in sheltered undergrowth, along old stone walls or in rocky areas.

The plant acquired its name because it was once used by butchers to sweep their blocks. It does not belong to the 'Broom' family, but is instead a close relative of asparagus. Like the latter, it is edible, and its young shoots continue to be used as a vegetable by country connoisseurs in some parts of Devon.

Medicinally, a contemporary cure from Dartmouth suggests that butchers' broom is still used in the treatment of jaundice and 'gravel'. Apparently, it should be gathered in the late summer and hung in a shady spot to dry; the leaves and stems should then be chopped up and stored in an airtight container. When necessary, an ounce may be infused in a pint of boiling water for ten minutes and the patient given a wineglassful morning and evening.

Sufferers from chilblains have used butchers' broom in what must have been a decidedly painful treatment for the condition. The plant –the nearest thing to a cactus which we have in Britain – was struck across the sores to open them up, and so presumably speed their recovery. The cure may have been worse than the chilblains themselves!

BUTTERCUP

(Ranunculus spp.)

- Chickens
- Crazy
- Fairies' Basins (Axminster)
- Goody-cup
- Gulp cap/cop

- Craw-tone
- Crazy
- Crow-toe
- Goody-cup

} Creeping Buttercup (R. repens)

The buttercup is one of our commonest wild flowers, carpeting meadows, waysides and waste ground with its sun-gold flowers. There are several varieties, between them flowering from early March to late September. The meadow buttercup (R. acris) can reach a majestic 90 cms, but its creeping cousin (R. repens) may be no taller than 5 or 10 cms, although it too can attain to greater heights. All have deeply divided leaves, which may be covered in hairs. The buttercup is a hardy flower, resisting man's best efforts – chemical or otherwise – to restrict its spread. Creeping buttercup is a particularly stubborn weed, as many gardeners will testify with feeling.

In the past, it was accredited with the ability both to cause and cure madness, and children were warned that if they smelt a buttercup they would become mad. On the other hand, it was considered that hanging the flower around the neck of a person who was mad, when the moon was on the wane, would cause that person to be restored to his or her right mind.

The sap of the buttercup, like that of the celandine, is caustic, and if it comes into contact with the skin it can be irritating. Undaunted by this fact, children continue to pick the flower as generations of others have done before them in order to carry out the 'butter-test': an open buttercup is picked and held under the chin of the person to be tested; if it reflects the golden colour of the bloom that person has a definite liking for butter!

CAMOMILE

(Anthemis nobilis)

Camomile was once widely found in herb gardens, often forming lawns or paths, for it has a pleasant 'apple' smell which is particularly noticeable when the plant is crushed. 'Camomile' is actually derived from two Greek words meaning 'earth-apple'. It flowers during the summer months, and has white, daisy-like flowers around a golden centre, and feathery leaves.

An old country adage says of this plant:-

'The camomile bed,
The more you tread it, the more it will spread.'

and although camomile lawns need careful attention, this is amply rewarded by the delicious scent given off whenever it is stepped upon. Such lawns need to be weeded by hand, for modern herbicides will kill them, and they must be cut before the flowers appear. Camomile is reputed to be a very good plant to have in a garden, for it seems to benefit all other plants growing around it.

William Browne considered it to be great value to fishes, also! Writing of some nymphs, he said:-

'Another from her banks in sheer good will,
Brings nutriment for fish, the camomile.'

It is humans, however, who have most reason to be grateful for this herb, for it has been used medicinally over many centuries. Devonians obviously considered camomile to be an excellent muscle relaxant, for local cures for cramp, running-gout and a stitch in the side all include it among their ingredients. The cures come from the Chudleigh area, and date from the seventeenth century:-

'For a stitch in the side: a wooden dish was filled with alternating layers of camomile and hot embers, and a linen cloth fixed over it. The dish was then held, as hot as could be borne, against the side of the body.

For cramp: an oil was made by boiling together camomile flowers, mallow leaves and parsley in butter or salad oil. The resulting embrocation was then rubbed into the muscle spasm.
For running gout: equal quantities of the oils of camomile, mallow, foxglove and dill were combined, and the mixture 'worked in well before the fire with a warm hand'.

Camomile is recommended as a tonic. The flowers should be picked without their stalks, as soon as they are fully opened, and then dried and stored. The tonic may be made by adding half an ounce of dried flowers to a pint of boiling water; after standing for ten minutes it should be strained and a wineglassful taken morning and night. The infusion will also bring relief from headaches.

Locally, the plant is often known as 'Bachelor's Button' from an old country custom whereby men carried this flower in their pockets to learn whether they would succeed with their sweethearts; apparently, if the flower kept its colour and did not fade, they would be successful.

Alternatively, if a girl was unsure which of her suitors she should marry, she would pick a flower for each one as a buttonhole. She would then watch to see which developed into the finest flower, and take this as an indication that she should choose its wearer.

CAMPION, RED

(Lychnis dioica)

- Adders' Flower
- Bachelor's Button
- Big Robin Hood
- Cock Robin
- Jandy Crowders
- Rabbit's Rose
- Red Bird's Eye
- Robert's Rose

The bright-pink flowers of the red campion are a familiar sight as they brighten hedgerows, waysides and woods, often persisting into late autumn in mild areas. The individual plants are of one sex only, so need to be near others of the opposite sex if the seed is to be fertilised. The flower is unperfumed, unlike its night-scented cousin, the white campion, *(L. alba),* but where the two varieties grow together they may fertilise one another, so hybrids of widely varying shades occur.

CELANDINE, GREATER

(Chelidonium majus)

- Cure-wort
- Kill-wart
- St. John's Wort
- Wart Flower

The greater celandine is a member of the poppy family, and its bright yellow flowers may be seen between April and October growing along the hedgerows, verges and waste areas of the county. The seeds are contained within long, distinctive pods, and produce an oil which is attractive to ants. By feeding upon it, the ants ensure that the seed becomes widely distributed.

The Latin name for it – *Chelidonium* – means 'Swallow-herb', and there is a story that the swallow restored sight to the eyes of her young when evil had befallen them by means of this plant. It was certainly thought to be valuable in the treatment of eye complaints in the last century: one local cure required that celandines should be pounded with salt, placed onto linen and laid on the inside of the wrist on the same side of the body as the sore eye. The flowers were to be changed twice daily, and the application continued until the eye was quite better. Under no circumstances should celandines be applied to the eye itself, however, for they contain a highly caustic juice which could cause extreme irritation.

This causticity accounts for another major use of the plant in the county, as revealed by its local names of 'Kill-wart' or 'Wart-Flower': the juice of the greater celandine was sqeezed onto the wart causing them to disappear quite rapidly.

The greater celandine is one of nature's weather-forecasters, for it closes its flower when dull weather is on the way, and opens again when the sun shines.

CELANDINE, LESSER

(Ranunculus ficaria)

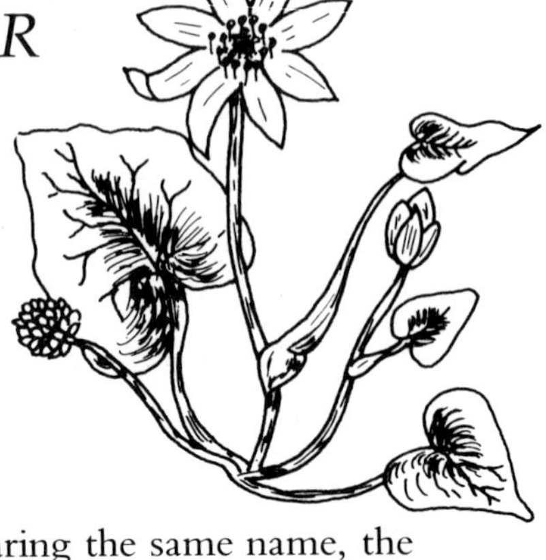

- Bright Eye
- Cream & Eggs
- Figwort
- Golden Cup
- Pilewort

Though both bearing the same name, the greater and lesser celandines belong to two quite different families, the former being a type of poppy, and the latter, a variety of buttercup. Lesser celandines appear early in the year between February and May, and may be found hugging the ground in damp and shady areas such as woods and meadows, banks and grassy verges. It is the early appearance of their golden-yellow flowers, flanked by the dark-green, heart-shaped leaves, which makes them such a welcome sight at the ending of each winter – hence their affectionate country-name of 'bright-eye'.

Another local name, 'Pilewort', reveals one of the traditional uses for this flower. Because the roots resemble a clump of haemorrhoids, the ancient herbalists considered this to be nature's way of informing us that the plant could be used to heal this condition. The roots were usually boiled in hog's lard and the resulting ointment rubbed into the affected area.

To others, the roots of the lesser celandine looked more like the udders of a cow, and so they were often to be found hanging in cowsheds, in the hope that their presence would cause the cream content of the milk to be greatly increased.

CLOVER
(Trifolium spp.)
– Iver

Country-folk believe that they can foretell the weather by observing the clover-plant: when rough to the touch, stormy and tempestuous weather may be expected; and if its leaves 'start up and rise, as if it were afraid of an assault', heavy rain is surely on its way.

Occasionally, plants may be found which have groups of more than three leaflets, and a popular superstition maintains that anyone who comes across a four-leaved clover without seeking it will be blessed with great good luck. In Devon young girls were convinced that if they found such a leaf they could be sure of seeing their true-love before the day was over. To dream of clover is also considered most fortunate, for it is a sign that health and good luck will remain with the dreamer.

There is one particular variety of clover – the Calvary Clover – which is characterised by red spots upon its leaves: these are said locally to have been caused by Christ's blood dripping onto the plant whilst he hung on the Cross on Mount Calvary. The association has been further strengthened by the fact that the dried seed-pod, when bent into circular form, resembles a miniature crown of thorns and the trefoliated leaf has been adopted as a symbol of the trinity.

COLTSFOOT *(Tussilago farfara)*

– Bull's foot
– Coughwort
– Son-before-father

Coltsfoot is a daisy-like, golden-yellow flower which blooms between February and May, cheering banks, waste-ground, clifftops and cultivated land, especially where the soil is clay. The plant is unusual in that the flowers appear before the leaves – hence its popular name of 'son-before-father'. The leaves, whose hoof-like appearance explains the plant's name, only develop when all signs of flowering are over.

Coltsfoot leaves have been used in the past to make a type of tobacco which was recommended for the relief of asthma – the generic name 'Tussilago' is derived from the Greek word for a cough. The tobacco could be made in various ways: the simplest was to gather the leaves in June or July, dry them for a few months and then flake them between

the fingers. A far superior flavour could be obtained by hanging the leaves in a warm, dry place until they resembled dry chamois leather, and then stripping away and discarding the central stalks. The leaves were then packed tightly into an earthenware container with a spoonful or two of brandy and left for about a month: thereafter they were removed in thin layers, rolled up and placed under a heavy weight for several days. The resulting 'tobacco' was now ready to be sliced and crumbled in the usual way.

COMFREY *(Symphytum officinale)*

– Gooseberry-pie
– Knitbone

Comfrey is a plant of damp and shady places. The curled sprays of nodding bell-like flowers, which appear in the early summer, may be white, cream, pink or purple, and grow out on short stalks from the tall, hairy stem. The large dark-green leaves are also covered with fine hairs.

The medicinal value of comfrey has been recognised for centuries. Amongst its properties is the ability to arrest bleeding: for this purpose it was bruised to a pulp and either boiled in milk or made to the consistency of treacle before being applied to the cut. It was also thought useful in cases of internal haemorrhage, when it was again boiled in milk and taken by mouth.

A resident of Ottery-St-Mary recalls that her father was once healed of a sprained ankle in 24 hours by means of comfrey root. The root was dug up and broken – 'dirt 'n all' – onto a piece of linen, which was then applied to the injured part. Apparently, in the case of a true sprain the poultice was supposed to stick and become quite hard, before falling off 24 hours later, when the sprain would be completely healed. A similar use of comfrey root in the county was in the treatment of injuries such as crushed fingers, etc.; once again, the root was crushed and bound around the injury, where if left for 9 days it was supposed to 'set it all back in place.'

The same plant was used by Lady Clifford of Ugbrooke House, Chudleigh, to treat a rupture in the seventeenth century. Her prescription required that a good handful of half red and half white comfrey should be stripped of stalks and dried to a powder, then put into a pint of white wine with two ounces of hard sugar. This should then be boiled in close covered earthen pot until half evaporated, and the sufferer given two spoonsful of the mixture on retiring, after his first sleep, and in the morning before food. Additionally, a good handful of the stalks should be boiled in a pint of thick cream until it emulsified, then strained and when cold spread onto new linen and applied to the injured part as a 'plaster'.

The healing powers of comfrey are reputed to be so great that it is even supposed to conceal a young girl's lost virginity from her husband-to-be! The night before the wedding the bride should soak for a long period in a bath to which comfrey had been added in generous quantities. There is a tale, dating from the middle-ages, of a maid who was to be married the next day, and who used this treatment to conceal her doubtful past from her future spouse. Since hot water was scarce, her mistress was reluctant to waste the chance of taking a comforting bath, and herself jumped into the still-hot tub: that night, her own husband was extremely surprised to find his wife once more a virgin!

COW-PARSNIP

(Heracleum sphondylium)

- Billers (Bere Ferrers; Hartland; Sutcombe)
- Caddell
- Cadweed
- Cake seed/Caxeys
- Eltrot
- Hogweed
- Humpy-scrumples
- Keck/Kex/Kexies
- Limpenskrimps
- Madnep
- Pig's Bubble/Cole/Flop
- Rabbit's Meat
- Scouter
- Snake's Meat
- Sweet Biller
- Umlick
- Wippul Squip

Cow-parsnip or Hogweed is a familiar sight for it grows abundantly in open woods, and along hedgerows and grassy verges. A member of the Parsley family, it can grow as tall as a man. The small white flowers which make up its flattened flower-head or umbel appear between June and September; the leaves are large, hairy and irregularly divided; and the stem, which is also hairy, is hollow and ridged.

In former times it was widely used as pig-fodder, hence its alternative name of 'hogweed', and local variations such as 'Pig's Bubble' and 'Pig's Flop'. The young leaves, when boiled, have a taste of asparagus, and country people were not averse to including them in their own diets from time to time.

Cow-parsnip shares a number of its local names, such as 'Eltrot', 'Kecks', 'Snakes Meat' and 'Rabbits Meat' with its close relative, the Cow-parsley. Although it was given the last of these names through being frequently gathered and fed to rabbits, it acquired the title 'Snakes Meat' for a different reason: quite harmless in themselves, cow-parsnip and cow-parsley look very like both Hemlock and Fools' Parsley, which are themselves deadly poisonous. A name which associated the plants with snakes would naturally serve as a warning that caution should be taken when picking them.

This association may help to explain the old Devon superstition voiced by an elderly lady from Torquay in the 1920s, which claimed that "tis ill taking kecks into the house.' The superstition may stem from the fact that the plant belongs to the same family as parsley, that herb of ill-repute which, despite its excellent medicinal properties, has become associated with Satan and his works, and hence regarded as a plant of evil omen. Another possible reason for the warning against picking hogweed for the house may be that especially in hot weather, it will often cause painful blistering if it comes into contact with the skin. Nevertheless, this has not prevented the hardy children of Devon from using its hollow stem as a pea-shooter!

COWSLIP *(Primula veris)*

- Boots & Shoes
- Cowflop
- Keys of Heaven
- Tisty-Tosty

It is becoming increasingly difficult to find the cowslip – that delicate, sweet-scented, deep-yellow relative of the primrose – growing in the wild. Once so common in the meadows and woodland of the county, it is said to be so called because it originally sprang up from dung which had 'slipped' from a cow! A rather more savoury legend maintains that it grew up on the spot where St. Peter dropped the keys to the gates of Heaven – hence its local name of 'Keys of Heaven'. The blooms, drooping down from their stalks, do somewhat resemble a bunch of keys, so this is probably how the legend arose.

'Tisty-tosty' is another country name for the cowslip, and refers to a very old children's game which involved a cowslip-ball made by tying the flower-clusters onto stretched string, and then pressing them together and knotting the string. The tisty-tosty was often used in love-divination: if a young girl wished to know the name of her husband-to-be she would toss the ball in the air and chant:-

'Tisty-tosty, tell me true
Who shall I be married to'.

While it was falling to earth she would call out the names of all the likely contenders, in the conviction that whichever name she was calling as the ball hit the ground would belong to her true love. Alternatively, she could recite the letters of the alphabet:-

'Tisty-tosty cowslip ball
At my sweethearts name you'll fall:
A, B, C, D............'

In this case, she would learn the initial of his name instead.

This practice of using cowslip to divine a true love is one which Robert Herrick obviously knew of, for a poem in the 'Hesperides' runs as follows:-

'I call, I call, who doe ye call?
The maids to catch this Cowslip-ball:
But since these Cowslips fading be,
Troth, leave the flowers, and Maids, take me.
Yet, if that neither you will doe,
Speak but the word, and Ile take you.'

Cowslip-flowers were once highly valued by women, for they could be used to make a skin tonic which would make the complexion 'splendent', as an old Devonian recipe declares. This called for cowslip blossoms and cucumber to be combined to make a lotion for use on the face: on no account should the leaves and stalk be included, however, for their juice can be highly irritating to certain skins.

Today, Cowslip-tea is recommended by country-folk for the relief of insomnia: two ounces of the flowers should be picked from their calyces and infused for ten minutes in a pint of boiling water; the infusion should then be strained and bottled. the correct dosage is one wineglassful, but this should only be taken when really necessary, for if used too frequently its effectiveness diminishes. Since the infusion will only keep for one week the flowers may be dried (out of artificial light or sunlight) and stored in an airtight jar until needed.

CUCKOO-PINT
(Arum maculatum)

- Adders' Meat (North Tawton)
- Adder's Tongue
- Cows & Calves
- Daddy-in-the-pulpit
- Dog's Dibble
- Kings & Queens
- Lamb-in-a-pulpit
- Lords & Ladies
- Parson & Clerk
- Parson-in-the -pulpit
- Poison Berries
- Poison Maur
- Soldiers & Angels
- Wild Arum
- Wild Lily

The Wild Arum is a familiar plant of local banks and hedgerows, and is best known for the clusters of bright red berries which appear from July onwards. The distinctive flowers are contained in a large, pale-green sheath edged with purple spots. Evident in the centre of this is a brownish-purple club-like structure which gives off a disgusting odour similar to that of decaying meat. The leaves of the cuckoo-pint grow from the base of the plant, are large, arrow-shaped and glossy. They are borne on long stalks, and may also be covered in purple spots.

Many of the local names for this plant obviously refer to its unusually-shaped

flower; for example, the dark 'club' in the centre of its pale sheath obviously reminded some locals of the parson speaking from his pulpit! But older associations are less innocent, for from medieval times the flower's appearance has caused it to be associated with the sexual act, as one of its most familiar names – 'Cuckoo-pint' – suggests, for 'cuckoo' is probably a corruption of 'cuckold' – an old word for a man whose wife has wronged him with another.

Local names such a 'Poison-berries' or 'Poison-maur' speak for themselves, for the berries are indeed poisonous, and can be deadly if eaten by children. It is probably as a warning against this that the Devon superstition associating the plant with snakes arose. In the area around North Tawton the wild arum is often referred to as 'Adder's Meat' or 'Adder's Tongue', and local children were taught that adders acquire their sting through eating it. They were therefore warned not to approach it too closely, for fear that a snake might be lurking nearby.

The Cuckoo-pint is also called 'Lords & Ladies' or 'Kings & Queens' because in Elizabethan times the ruffs and collars of the aristocracy were stiffly starched, often with the substance contained in its root. It was, however, highly irritant and caused painful blistering on the hands of the unfortunate laundresses.

DAFFODIL

(Narcissus pseudo narcissus)

- Bell Rose
- Cowslip/Cowslop
- Cuckoo-Rose
- Daffadowndilly
- Easter Lily
- Giggary
- Goose-Flop
- Gracey/Greasey Daisy
- Hoop Petticoat
- Lentil's
- Lent Lily
- Lent Rose
- Lenticup

Who could fail to be cheered by the sight of daffodils coming into bloom in February? We are fortunate in Devon in that, as well as the familiar garden varieties, we still have wild daffodils blossoming in our woods and

meadows, riverbanks and damp, grassy areas. The wild daffodil is smaller than its garden relative, but just as easily recognisable.

Despite their beauty daffodils, like bluebells and primroses, were one of the flowers which Devonians were wary of bringing into the house of anyone who kept poultry – hence the local name for the flower of 'gooseflop'. An inhabitant of Buckland Brewer in the 1870s stated adamantly: 'daun't bring they giggarys in 'ouze; vor if ee du, es shan't ha a zingle chick, vor the eggs under the owld hen'll be all addled.' In Christow and the Teign Valley it was thought quite acceptable to pick a large bunch of these flowers for the house, for here they believed that the number of eggs hatched would be equivalent to the number of daffodils in the bunch. The superstition still existed in South Molton in the 1930s.

Robert Herrick saw this flower as a portent of his own life. In his 'Divination by a Daffodil' he wrote:

'When a daffodil I see
Hanging down his head t'wards me;
Guess I may what I must be;
First I shall decline my head;
Secondly I shall be dead;
Lastly, safely buried.'

DAISY *(Bellis perennis)*

– Gracy daisy
– Hens and Chickens

The name 'daisy' is a corruption of a much older word – 'Day's Eye' – so called because the flower opens its petals at dawn and closes them again at dusk. Robert Herrick described it in his poem 'To daisies:

'Shut not so soon; the dull-eyed night
Has not as yet begun
To make a seizure on the light
Or to seal up the sun.

No marigolds yet closed are;
No shadows great appear;
Nor doth the early Sheperd's Star
Shine like a spangle here...'

It is not certain whether the generic name 'bellis' is derived from the Latin for 'beautiful' – which it certainly is – or for 'war'. The latter meaning is quite possible for daisies were used to staunch bleeding wounds on the battlefield.

The daisy has traditionally been considered an emblem of modesty, and was one of the flowers used by young girls to divine the true affections of their lovers – the petals were picked off one by one, 'he loves me, he loves me not...' until the last one settled the issue.

There can be few country girls who have never made a daisy chain and then worn it around their neck, but how many know of the very old Devon superstition which maintains that any child wearing a daisy-chain is safe from fairy kidnapping?

In Bridestowe, in the early part of this century, daisies featured in a charm for boils. The sufferer was required to crawl around a field on hands and knees picking the heads off the flowers and eating them – three on the first morning, five on the second, and so on until the boils disappeared!

DANDELION

(Taraxacum vulgare)

– Four o'clocks (Axminster)
– Milky Dashle
– Piss-a-bed

Dandelions are one of our commonest wild flowers, to be found blooming on roadsides, grassy areas and waste ground at any time between March and October. In gardens they can be a troublesome weed, but to the unjaundiced eye they appear as handsome golden-yellow flowers. The flowerheads are crowded with up to 200 narrow florets, followed by as many 'parachutes' of seeds forming the familiar dandelion 'clock'. The hollow stems are filled with 'milk', and it is the shape of the leaves which has given rise to the name 'dandelion', for this word is a corruption of the old French name for the flower – 'dents-de-lion', or 'lion's teeth'. It is true that the serrated leaves do somewhat resemble the teeth of this mighty beast.

In Axminster, the dandelion is often called a 'four o'clock', because it closes up when the light begins to fail in the early evening. The seed 'clocks' can also be used to tell the time, at least according to young children everywhere. They blow upon them and either count the number of seeds left sticking to the head, or alternatively count the number of blows it takes to remove every seed. In either case, the total is said to tally with the hour of the day. Dandelion flowers also close in poor weather, and country folk claim that a dandelion closing in the middle of the day is a sure sign of a coming storm. Similarly, if the seed-down falls off a dandelion 'clock' when there is no wind, this may be taken as an indication that rain is on the way.

Another widespread nickname for this

flower is the 'piss-a-bed', referring to the old superstition that any child who picks a dandelion will end the day by wetting the bed! It is certainly true that the plant is an excellent bladder-stimulant, which has for many centuries been used to treat cases of cystitis or water-retention: for this purpose the young leaves were gathered and eaten fresh.

Since dandelions have always been widely available in the wild, country folk exploited their value in culinary as well as medicinal recipes. Tender, chopped leaves make a tasty salad, or alternatively may be lightly boiled and eaten as 'greens'.

These flowers were one of the ingredients of a sovereign remedy for 'keeping-away illness' which was known in Stockleigh Pomeroy. It advised that one should regularly drink an infusion of dandelion leaves, watercress and stinging-nettles if one wished to remain in good health.

From the Chudleigh area in the seventeenth century comes a brew for 'Sweetening the Blood', made by taking 2 handfuls each of dandelion leaves, fumitory, hartstongue, agrimony, brooklime and watercress. To these were added 4 handfuls of fir tops, 1 oz each of angelica and sea-holly root, and ¾ pint each of dried orange and lemon. The ingredients were gently bruised and distilled with 3 pints of a posset made with Rhenish wine. The dosage was 12 spoonfuls to be taken morning and evening.

Dandelions were also of value in the treatment of corns, according to an Exeter lady. The corn should first be cut out or removed with a corn plaster. In order to kill the root generous quantities of dandelions should be gathered and the white fluid squeezed onto pieces of linen placed over the site of the corns and kept there for five days without being disturbed; should it be necessary to wash the feet this should be done very carefully, so that the linen dressings are not wetted. If the cure does not work the first time, it will certainly be effective if repeated; however, the lady who reported the treatment said that she had never known of anyone who needed to try a second time.

Besides corns, dandelion 'milk' is also said to remove warts, spots and pimples if dabbed directly onto them. Care should be taken to ensure that the caustic liquid does not touch healthy skin, or irritation could follow.

Use may also be made of the dandelion root, for if chopped up and lightly roasted it makes a good substitute 'coffee'. As well as being tasty and non-stimulant, this coffee has the added benefit of preventing constipation. It may be made by digging up some fairly large plants, removing the greenstuff (which may be stewed or used in salad) and scrubbing the roots well. These should then be chopped up into pieces about the size of a normal coffee-bean, and laid on a baking sheet in an oven which has been preheated to Gas 6, (400°F, 200°C.) After an hour the roots should be brown, crisp, and ready to be ground up for use. The coffee is then made in the usual way, a reasonable strength being 3 level tablespoons to one pint of boiling water.

DILL *(Anethum graveolens)*

This plant has magical associations, for it is one of those which Devonian folklore sometimes features as a link between the human and spirit worlds. Thus it was said that the combined juices of dill, vervain and St. John's Wort, if used to anoint the eyes for three days in succession, would enable one to see the spirits of the air.

In tales of witchcraft, dill is frequently mentioned as an ingredient of spells, both those cast by witches and those conjured against them. There was a strong belief that plants favoured by magicians and powerful for evil in their hands had equal power to avert evil when used in charms against sorcery: dill was just such a plant. An old rhyme states that:-

'Vervain and dill
Hinder witches from their will'

Medicinally, dill water has been found effective in the relief of infantile flatulence and upset digestion. To make it, half an ounce of dill seed is infused in a pint of boiling water and allowed to stand for ten minutes: the mixture is then strained and bottled, and a teaspoonful given to the baby when required. The name 'dill' is in fact derived from the Norse word 'dilla', which means to lull or soothe – the exact effect which it has upon an infant with an upset stomach.

DOCK *(Rumex spp.)*

Dock belongs to the same family as sorrel, and grows indiscriminately on waste or cultivated ground, heaths and grassy areas.

There is a country superstition which maintains that a dock plant can always be found growing near to a clump of nettles.

Since dock is the natural antidote to nettle-stings, this has always been taken as evidence of Mother Nature's bounty. In Devon, children were often taught that chanting a special rhyme while massaging the dock-leaf over the stings would greatly increase its effectiveness. The rhyme went as follows:

'Nettle in, dock out
Dock rub nettle out.'

In parts of the county, dock tea was considered to be a very good remedy for boils: this rather unpalatable beverage was made by boiling the root of the plant well, straining the brew and drinking a wineglassful at a time.

Gardeners who find docks a troublesome weed might care to take a tip from a gentleman in North Devon. His garden seemed to be over-run by them, until one year he planted a bed of phlox. Thereafter, the docks never reappeared!

ELDER *(Sambucus nigra)*

– Bitter-flower (Axminster)

The elder is a tree of mixed reputation. Devonians consider it most unlucky either to bring it into the house, or to burn its wood; indeed, it is said in Moretonhampstead that 'if you burn elder, you skin a sheep' (i.e. you cause its death). The warning is a sound one, for elder spits in a most dangerous fashion when set alight – so much so that in former times this was said to be caused by the Devil spitting down the chimney!

Nevertheless, country people also consider this tree to be a protection against witches, self-sown elder being especially powerful against evil, and continue the practice of fastening a cross made from it to the walls of cow houses to keep all harm away from the animals. In addition, it was popularly thought that elder can never be struck by lightning.

The reason for these conflicting ideas can probably be traced back to the old belief that it was the elder which provided both the wood for the Holy Cross, and the tree from which Judas hanged himself – a good example of the way in which superstition and religious belief have become intermingled.

Locally, the tree is known as 'Bitter-flower' for the leaves have a bitter and unpleasant smell and were often worn in the hat to keep away flies.

At the beginning of the century children in parts of Devon used to make 'pop-guns' out of elder: they would force a hole through the pith, and then fashion a ram-rod out of hazel wood. Chewed paper would be rammed down the hollowed elder sticks, and pressed out with considerable force. Great sport ensued!

Elder berries provided an early form of hair-dye, and were used by women to colour their hair inky-black. The dye was permanent, and could also be used on cloth. Elder leaves, too, gave a green dye, but this had to be mordanted, or fixed, with chrome.

Medicinally, elder was one of the ingredients in a seventeenth century Chudleigh preventative against the plague: a handful each of elder leaves, sage and rue were pounded, strained with a quart of white wine, and mixed with a little ginger and a spoonful of treacle. This was then drunk morning and evening.

Elder buds have been used in the past in the treatment of inflammation, fever, influenza and colds: a double handful of dried buds was placed with the same amount of peppermint into a teapot, and 1-2 pints of boiling water added. The brew was infused for 30 minutes, and then strained. It was now ready to be drunk freely, sweetened with honey or black treacle.

More recently, elder flowers have been recommended for anyone suffering from bronchitis: the flowers, either fresh or dried, should be infused for ten minutes and the resulting tea drunk at regular intervals. This will induce perspiration, and also help loosen the chest and make coughing easier and more productive. Elderberry juice or jelly is also said to be soothing, and is particularly good in cases of quinsy.

The leaves of the elder are supposed to bring relief from nettle-stings, and also encourage the healing of leg sores if bandaged in place. Chewed, it is claimed that they also relieve toothache.

And for constipation, one should take powdered elder bark infused in hot water, according to a report from East Devon.

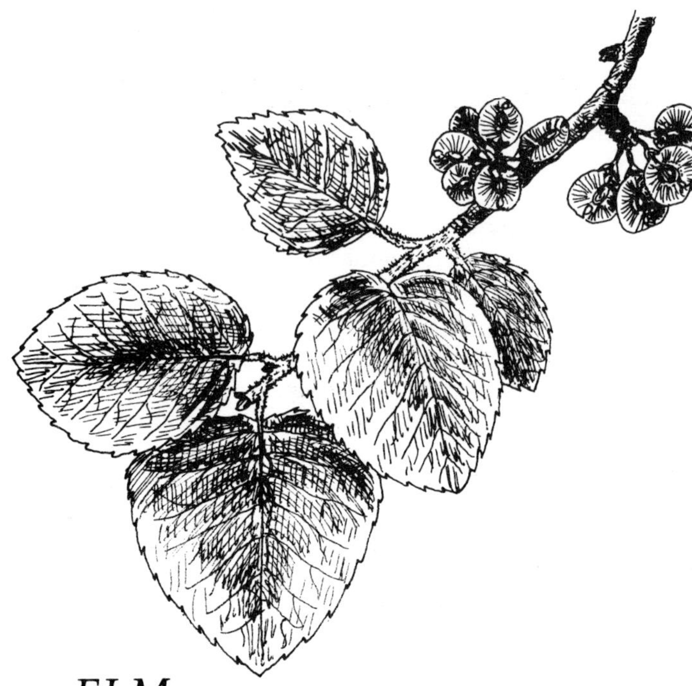

ELM (*Ulmus procera*)

The mighty English Elm was one of the earliest trees known in Devon, for together with the oak, it probably established itself here about six or seven thousand years ago. However, it did not really become a familiar tree until the seventeenth century when it became fashionable to plant it along hedgerows and in parkland. Selective breeding produced trees which would grow to a uniform height and remain in leaf until late autumn, but this unfortunately meant that all the trees were genetically similar, so that when the tragedy of Dutch Elm Disease struck the English Elm it was able to spread unchecked.

Thus, it may soon become impossible for Devon farmers and gardeners to look to the Elm as they did in the past, in order to learn the correct times for sowing and planting certain things. A local rhyme gives the following advice:-

'When the elm leaf is as big as a mouse's ear
Then to sow barley never fear;
When the elm leaf is as big as an ox's eye,
Then I say 'Hie, bags Hie';
When elm leaves are as big as a shilling,
Plant kidney beans if to plant them you are willing;
When elm leaves are as big as a penny
You must plant kidney beans if you mean to have any.'

FIGWORT (*Scrophularia nodosa*)

– Brown-Nut
– Crowdy-Kit
– Fiddles
– Fiddlestick
– Poor Man's Salve
– Throatwort

Few would guess from its appearance that Figwort was once an important medicinal herb. Its flowers are small and dingy; its smell unpleasant to humans but attractive to wasps, and its long leaves pointed and toothed. The plant is found mainly in damp woods and along the riverbanks of Devon.

As its local name of 'Poor Man's Salve' suggests, the Figwort was found to have the power to heal skin eruptions, abscesses and ulcers: the leaves and stem were made into a poultice which relieved pain wherever applied.

The plant's generic name, 'Scrophularia' reveals another conditon which it was once used to treat, namely the dreaded King's Evil, or scrophula. This was a tuberculous disease characterised by tumorous swellings in the glands of the neck, which accounts for the Figwort being widely known as 'Throatwort'.

FORGET-ME-NOT

(Myositis arvensis)

– Bugloss
– Mouse-Ear

From about April the tiny, bright-blue flowers of the forget-me-not with their butter-yellow eye are a most attractive sight along hedgerows and banks, in woods, and on waste or cultivated ground.

In medieval times this modest little flower was accorded with the supernatural ability to open secret caverns wherein lay hidden treasures. It was said that if the flower was pressed against the side of the rock behind which the riches were to be found, an opening would immediately appear.

Local blacksmiths often used to keep bunches in their forge, for they believed that to do so would protect the horses from being accidentally injured whilst being shod.

Medicinally, forget-me-nots were once used to treat coughs and other forms of chest complaints.

FLEABANE

(Pulicaria (Inula) dysenterica)

– Camels

The golden-yellow, daisy-like flowers of the Fleabane brighten the marshes and wetter meadows of Devon from July to September. This plant's principal virtue is revealed in its name, for it has long been used as a most effective flea-repellent: indeed, its generic name is also derived from the Latin word 'pulex', meaning 'flea'. It was most used in the days when it was the custom to strew the floors of dwellings with rushes which frequently harboured these bugs, and Devon housewives found that burning a handful of fleabane daily would serve to keep the house free of them. It had the added bonus of deterring flies as well.

FOXGLOVE *(Digitalis purpurea)*

- Cow-flop (Hartland)
- Finger-hut
- Flop (Hartland)
- Flop-dock (Sutcombe)
- Flop-top
- Fropadock
- Hedge-poppy (Axminster)
- Hollyhock (Hawkchurch)
- Long Purples (Moretonhampstead)
- Pixy-glove
- Pop-dock (Moretonhampstead)
- Purples (Moretonhampstead)
- Rabbit's Flower
- Thor's Mantle
- Virgin's Fingers

The pinky/purple flower spikes of the foxglove covered with up to eighty thimble-shaped flowers, are a handsome sight wherever they occur – along roadside-verges, railway banks, on heaths and in woods. Closer inspection shows that the flowers, which appear between June and August, have a paler inside covered in purple spots. The leaves are large, oval and quilted, and like the stem are grey-green and covered in fine down.

The origin of the name 'Foxglove' is uncertain, but one legend maintains that the pixies tied the bell-shaped blooms onto the paws of foxes to muffle their steps during raids on chicken-houses. Alternatively 'fox' glove could be a corruption of 'folk's' glove, the folk in question being the fairies or little-people – hence the local name for the flower of 'pixy-glove'.

Digitalis, extracted from the foxglove, is today one of the most important drugs used in the treatment of heart disease, for it slows, steadies and strengthens the heart-beat. The scientist who isolated the drug in 1785, William Withering, became interested in the plant when he observed country women successfully treating dropsy with foxglove tea. Nevertheless, the plant is recognised today as being extremely POISONOUS, and should never be taken internally, unless under careful medical supervision.

At the end of the last century, a Devon remedy recommended the use of foxgloves, which had to be gathered on the north side of a hedge, in the treatment of skin sores – the plants being applied externally.

GOOSEBERRY *(Ribes grossularia)*

– Goose-Gog

A Devonian belief from the 1880s maintains that if it is a good year for gooseberries, it will be a poor one for apples.

Gooseberries figure in a Great Torrington charm for warts from the beginning of this century. Prickles – one for each wart – were taken from a gooseberry bush and stuck well into each wart: the prickles were then collected and buried, so that as they rotted the warts disappeared.

A curious superstition, known in many parts of the county, reports that if a dead cat is planted beneath a smooth-fruited gooseberry-bush, then the following year the fruit will be covered in hairs!

GOOSE-GRASS *(Galium aparine)*

– Burr
– Cleavers
– Cli/Cly (Axminster)
– Cling-Rascal
– Clyders (Sutcombe)
– Duck's Meat (Hartland)
– Sticky-Button
– Sweet-hearts

Most of the local names for this plant– 'cleavers', 'cling-rascal', 'sticky-button' or 'sweethearts' – refer to the clinging nature of its hooked seeds, but according to one Devonian superstition they will only cling to a person who is in love. Thus if someone is seen sporting burrs, this may be taken as a sure sign that he or she has a sweet-heart, despite all protestations to the contrary.

Another use for goose-grass seeds was known to past generations of Honiton lace-makers, for they used them to adorn their pins.

This plant acquired its name because at one time it was a major source of food for geese, and since in Hartland it is also known as 'duck's meat' it was probably fed to these birds as well. However, in poorer rural areas it was also used for human consumption: the young shoots were included in soups, or were lightly boiled as a green vegetable, and being rich in Vitamin C helped to prevent scurvy. Goose-grass is in fact related to coffee, and an excellent substitute for the real thing can be made by gathering the seeds, drying them and then roasting them lightly. A tea, made by infusing the whole plant in boiling water for about ten minutes, was often given to anyone suffering from a cold: its chief benefit was the ability to induce a sound and peaceful sleep.

In the last century, goose-grass was used in Devon in the treatment of tumours and cancers. It has a stimulating effect on bladder and bowels, and was one of the most famous 'slimming-aids' of the past. The sixteenth century herbalist, John Gerarde, wrote that 'women do make a potage of the cleavers with some oatmeal to cause lanknesse and keep them from fatnesse'. It continues to be prescribed today for bladder-infections and water-retention.

GORSE *(Ulex europaeus)*

- French Fuzz
- Furze
- Whin

The brilliant yellow gorse grows abundantly on the heaths and commons of the County, and forms a dense shrub up to 3m tall. It does well on light soils, for the sharp, rigid spines which comprise its leaves are well able to conserve moisture. The attractive, scented flowers are evident throughout the year, and the seeds are borne in capsules which can be heard bursting on hot, summer days.

Because gorse flowers for much of the year, a number of superstitions have developed around it. One, widespread throughout the country, maintains that whilst it blossoms, England can never be conquered. Locally, however, its long season is given a much more light-hearted significance, for it is said that:

'Furze is only out of bloom
When kissing's out of tune'.

And if the furze blossom is at its most beautiful when the Spring comes, is this not the traditional time when 'young men's fancies lightly turn to thoughts of love'? The plant has been adopted as a symbol of constancy among Devon lovers, who hoped that their love would remain as steadfast.

But it was considered unlucky in Devon for a younger sister to marry before the older one, so if this should happen a special ceremony had to be enacted to avert the bad luck. This ceremony was known as 'Dancing the Furze Faggot'. After the wedding a small faggot, or bundle of furze was placed over the threshold of the bride's former home; the elder, unmarried sister ceremonially stepped over the faggot on her return to the house, hence, symbolically overcoming the obstacle to her own marriage.

Another local superstition maintains that it is extremely unlucky to bring gorse into the house in May, for it was believed that such an action would result in the death of a member of the household. Thus, although gorse is an excellent fuel, Devonians were very careful not to burn it indoors during this month.

Most people like the scent of gorse, but one notable exception was Robert Herrick, as his poem, 'The Custard' reveals:-

'For second course, last night, a custard came
To th'board, so hot, as none co'd touch the same;
Furze, three or four times with his cheeks did blow
Upon the custard, and thus cooled so:
It seemed by this time to admit the touch;
But none co'd eat it, 'cause it stunk so much.'

Furze had an important part to play in the Christmas decorations of poorer families in the county, for it was used to make the 'Kissing Bush', a substitute for mistletoe. A small furze bush would be dipped in water and then powdered with flour to give the impression of a snowy covering: it would be 'planted' in a pot which had been covered with silver paper, and holly berries would be spiked all over it. Finally, various sparkling powders might be sprinkled on the bush to improve the effect. It is not known whether this custom persists in Devon today, for the last reported use of a 'kissing-bush' comes from Chudleigh Knighton in the 1950's.

GROUND IVY *(Nepeta hederecea)*

- Ale Hoof
- Cat Mint
- Devil's Candlestick
- Hay Maids
- Rabbit's Meat
- Rat's Foot (Axminster)
- Rat's Mouths

Ground ivy, despite its name, belongs to the same family as mint, and if its kidney-shaped, toothed leaves are bruised they give off a distinctly minty aroma. The attractive, lilac-coloured flowers appear between March and June trailing along grassy verges and banks, or carpeting waste-ground and woodland.

The local name 'Ale Hoof' is interesting because it refers back to a time when ground ivy, and not hops, was added to beer during brewing. Even the introduction of hops to England in the sixteenth century did not cause the custom to die out, for some still preferred the flavour of the old drink, known as 'gill-ale'.

In the realms of magic ground ivy was once believed to have been dedicated to Satan, and it still bears the name of 'Devil's Candlestick' in some parts of the county.

However, despite any associations with the powers of darkness, ground ivy has long been valued for its medicinal properties. It used to be the custom to gather it in Spring and brew it into a tonic herbal tea which was said to drive away the last vestiges of winter ills, and to be especially good for clearing up lingering chesty coughs.

Ground ivy was also recommended in cases of eczema or minor skin sores. Its leaves were boiled in lard, and the resulting ointment cooled and rubbed into the skin.

In Stockleigh Pomeroy in the 1870s, this plant was one of the main ingredients in a cure for toothache – a complaint which, perhaps due to the acidity of our local cider, was very common in the last century. A Tavistock lady wrote in the 1830s that 'it is common to see young women with not a sound front tooth in their heads; and thus many a handsome face is thus spoilt and looks old before its time.' This particular remedy required that equal quantities of ground ivy root, pud-nettle root, leaves of rosemary and salt should be cut up small, crushed and packed into the cavity of the tooth, or if there was no cavity, laid across the jaw where the pain was most severe.

GROUNDSEL

(Senecio vulgaris)

- Bird's Eye
- Ground Swell

Groundsel, that tiny relative of the dandelion, thrives on any waste or cultivated ground and has become one of our commonest weeds, in flower from January to December.

Although today it is mainly gathered by children to feed to their pet rabbits, at one time it was highly valued as a medicinal herb. It was recommended in Chudleigh whenever the need arose for 'a vomit'. The groundsel was mixed with lukewarm posset ale (hot milk curdled by the addition of ale, and usually spiced); however it was stipulated that the leaves should be plucked 'downwards for a purge, and upwards for a vomit.'

In Tiverton in the early part of this century, groundsel was combined with parsley in the relief of 'water-stoppage' in both humans and animals: a double-handful of each plant was boiled in water, which was then strained and drunk – the dose being a pint for a man, and four pints for an animal.

A recent cure for Poll-Evil has been reported from North Devon: the eruption between a horse's ears or shoulders, known as 'Festilow' may be cured by boiling groundsel in water for 12 hours and applying the resulting liquor to the sores: the liquor may be bottled, and the condition should normally clear up within six weeks.

HAWTHORN

(Crataegus monogyna)

- Aggle
- Chucky-Cheese
- Eagles
- Eagle-Berry
- Haggle/Haigle/Hag/Haw
- Peggle
- May Blossom

The deciduous Hawthorn must be one of the commonest of all wayside shrubs, for it has been widely used to provide sturdy, impenetrable hedges. The clusters of small, white flowers, with their rather sickly scent, are a familiar sight each May. They are followed by the 'haws', the deep red fruits which are a rich source of food for the birds who winter in our region. The leaves are deeply divided.

The official name for the hawthorn – 'crataegus' – comes from the Greek word 'kratos', meaning 'strength', and testifies to the durability of the wood which in past times was used for carving. The tree has its place in history, for it was adopted as the badge of the Royal House of Tudor, supposedly because after the death of Richard III on Bosworth Field, Lord Stanley found his crown resting upon a hawthorn bush and placed it on the head of his son-in-law, the future King Henry VII.

Devonians consider it extremely unlucky to bring hawthorn into the house: in Torquay in the 1920s such a rash act was thought to be tempting Providence, and it was believed that a member of the household was sure to fall ill as a result of it. In Newton Abbot the consequences were held to be direr still, for at the beginning of the century it was believed that death would follow the bringing indoors of hawthorn blossom. And in nineteenth century Crediton grave misfortune, death or removal was expected to result from the cutting down of this bush. Such superstitions probably date back to the conviction that hawthorn had been used to fashion Christ's Crown of Thorns.

This must explain, too, the local legends of Christmas-flowering thorns akin to the famous one at Glastonbury. Towards the end of the last century, Lady Rosalind Northcote of Pynes wrote of one at Kenn which blossomed only on Christmas Day. Apparently the thorn, which stood on a plot of ground known as 'Holy Ground', had four legs pointing North, South, East and West. Late on Christmas Day it would burst into flower, the blossoms being snowy-white and covering the branches entirely. Within a few hours they faded, and although the tree would leaf normally in Spring, it would not bloom again until the following Christmas. For several years the thorn produced neither flower nor leaf, and the farmer to whom it belonged, presuming it to be dead, ordered its branches to be cut off and placed upon the fire. Immediately there was such a blaze that the house, stables and outhouses were all razed to the ground. They were never rebuilt, and the stock of the tree was dug up. The whole area became a wilderness of nettles and 'dassels' (thistles).

In the 1950s efforts were made to pinpoint the exact location of the 'Holy Ground'; noone then living in Kenn had heard of the legend, and although a number of cottages and farms in this area had been burnt down, none seemed to fit the details exactly. However, Lower Thornton, near Haldon, was destroyed in this manner and never rebuilt, so remains a possible candidate. The name 'Lower Thornton' may perhaps contain a

memory of this remarkable tree.

There was a similar thorn in the grounds of Clooneaven House, Lynmouth. This, too, burst into vigorous bloom for a few hours at Christmastide, only to fade rapidly. Apparently this thorn went on to produce not only leaves, but also flowers at the normal time in Spring. Yet another Christmas flowering thorn could be found in the grounds of Tavistock Abbey.

Although an ancient Kingsbridge superstition maintained that it was unlucky for Hawthorn to be in bloom before the first of May, 'May-Blossom' was an important ingredient of the May-Day celebrations. The Devon poet, William Browne, welcomed its appearance in these lines from the 'Britannia Pastorals':

> *'Mark the faire blooming of the Hawthorn tree,*
> *Who, finely clothed in a robe of white*
> *Fills full the wanton eye with May's delight.'*

For many, the sight of the hawthorn in bloom revives a hope of fine weather to come, and the country adage 'Cast not a clout till May is out' is held by many Devonians, used to a milder climate than more northerly parts of the country, to refer not to the month of May, but to May-blossom itself.

In Hartland it was believed that one could foretell the season's birth-rate from the number of hawthorn berries that year. A local rhyme asserted:

> *'Many nits, many pits,* (*'Many nuts, many graves*
> *Many sloans, many groans,* *Many sloes, much sickness,*
> *Many aggles, many cradles.'* *Many haws, many births.'*)

In similar vein, the severity of the coming winter was indicated:-

> *'Many haws*
> *Many sloes*
> *Many cold toes.'*

Hawthorn berries, which may be eaten straight from the bush, have the reputation of being an excellent tonic for sufferers from heart complaints. The young leaves have long been eaten by children, and account for the plant's local name of 'chucky-cheese'.

HAZEL *(Corylus avellana)*

- Halse-Nut
- Hedge-Fruits
- Nit-Alse
- Nut Arl (Sutcombe)
- Slip-Shell/Shawl (Moretonhampstead)
- Cat-O-Nine-Tails (Hazel catkins)
- Pussycats' Tails (Hazel catkins)

In past times hazelnuts were used by young girls in Devon as tools of divination, and they feature in a particular party-game. Each girl would put a hazelnut on the bar of the grate: the first girl to marry would be the one whose nut caught fire the quickest. A nut which cracked before blazing indicated that its owner would be jilted; and one which smouldered foretold a short, single and unhappy life; one which jumped off the bar promised a life of travel rather than marriage.

In 1902 an elderly lady practised an ancient custom at a wedding in Lewtrenchard. She approached the bridegroom in the church porch and presented him with a white bag filled with hazelnuts and tied up with green silk ribbon; this gift was supposed to bring good luck and a large family to the happy couple.

The association between nuts and fertility is a common one; a Sidmouth saying from the 1920s affirmed: 'good nutting, good bastards', suggesting that a good nut-harvest predicted a good crop of infants! But in Hartland it had a much more sinister significance, for here they believed that 'many nits (nuts)' meant 'many pits (graves)'.

According to an old Devon interpretation to dream of nuts is fortunate, for it indicates that money is on its way to you.

Hazel-sticks have long been used in the art of water-divining, and in the Westcountry have also been found useful in locating veins of metal such as copper or tin: a Y-shaped branch is cut, and the two 'arms' held loosely in the hands, keeping the branch parallel to the horizon. In principle, the 'foot' of the Y should dip down when the metallic lode is passed over, although in some instances it may shoot skywards instead. Ideally, sticks for this purpose should be cut on St. John's Eve or Night.

According to a superstition held in Exeter in the 1870s, and in Lewtrenchard in the early 1900s, those finding a double hazel-nut should carry it at all times in their pocket to ensure they never suffer from toothache.

HEATHER *(Calluna vulgaris)*

– Broom
– Heath
– Ling

'Calluna' is derived from the Greek 'to brush' and describes an early use of the plant, for heather brooms were very widely used in country areas. The heather would be cut in Spring when the twigs were green and pliant, for in that state they would shed neither leaves nor bark-dust. The bundles would be clamped and securely tied with strips of ash, and the ends squared off. A handle fashioned from ash, hazel or beech would be securely fixed to the head, and the broom would be ready for use.

Devon housewives would not allow a new heather broom to be introduced into the house during the month of May, for they were convinced that such an action would cause one of the family to be swept away!

Heather was also used in thatching, basket-making, and as an early and important source of fuel and is commonly referred to as 'ling', a word derived from the Anglo-Saxon 'lig', meaning 'fire'. It could also be made to yield an orange dye, so was used for colouring wool and cloth.

HERB ROBERT

(Geranium robertianum)

– Arb Rabbit
– Biscuits
– Candlesticks
– Cry Baby
– Dolly's Apron/Nightcap/Pinafore/Shoes
– Granny's Nightcap
– Hens & Chickens
– Jenny Hood
– Little Robin
– Mary Janes
– Robert's Bill
– Robin's flower
– Round Robin
– Soldiers
– Star of Bethlehem
– Wren's Flower

Herb Robert is an attractive deep-pink flower of banks, hedgerows, walls and stony areas. Behind its name, and such local variations as 'Robert's Bill', 'Robin's Flower' and 'Round Robin', the old legend of Robin

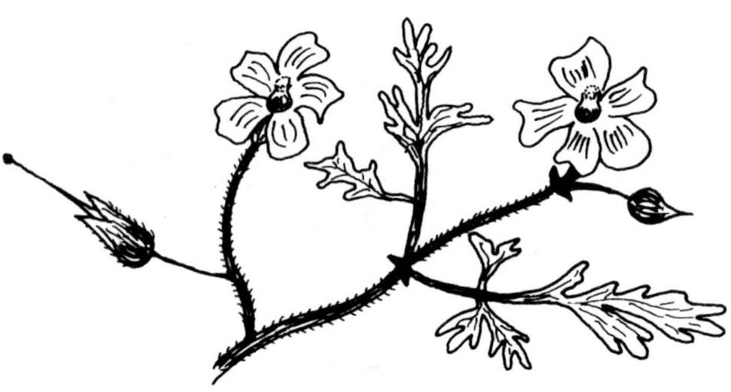

Goodfellow may probably be detected. He is reputed to have been a hobgoblin who used his powers to play sly pranks on evil-doers, and to give aid to honest folks.

Since its little flowers drop at night or during dull weather, country people considered Herb Robert to be one of nature's weather-forecasters.

It has had its medicinal uses, too, and was recommended for the treatment of stomach upsets such as diarrhoea, and said to be good for gout. Bruises and skin problems could also be treated by the application of a poultice made from its boiled leaves. Finally, medieval herbalists saw its deep red stems and ruddy leaves as an indication that it must be effective in curing blood disorders, and often used it to staunch bleeding.

HOLLY *(Ilex aquifolium)*

- Christmas
- Crocodiles

Devonshire knows many superstitions concerning the Holly Tree. It has variously been considered to be a plant of evil omen, a talisman, and means of forecasting the long-term weather prospects. The people of Moretonhampstead maintained in the last century that 'if holly berries be plentiful it will be a severe winter', and the belief persists to this day.

Severe ill-luck is supposed to follow the burning of holly, according to a Hartland superstition from the 1920s, and it is generally thought inadvisable either to bring it into the house before Christmas, or to leave it there afterwards. Just when the Christmas season ends and the decorations should be removed has been disputed, however. It has been said that holly berries should never be taken down before the feast of the Holy Innocents (28th December) when they should be fed to the birds. Most people today would probably agree with the Plymothians that Twelfth Night is the proper time, but Robert Herrick's 'Ceremonies upon Candlemas Eve' suggests that the 1st February was the day set aside for bidding an end to the Christmas festivities:-

'Down with the Rosemary and so
Down with the Bayes and Mistletoe:
Down with the Holly, Ivy, all,
Wherewith ye drest the Christmas Hall;
That so the superstitious find
No one least branch there left behind:
For look how many leaves there be
Neglected there (maids trust to me)
So many Goblins you shall see.'

Holly was widely believed to have a protective effect: it was said that lightning could never strike anyone under a holly tree, and it was considered to be very unlucky to cut such a tree down, particularly one that had seeded itself – some old leases contained specific clauses forbidding the destruction of hedgerow hollies. When, in the 1950s, two holly trees were cut down in the parish of Chittlehampton locals protested violently, saying that this would produce poltergeist havoc. And in Diptford in the mid-1960s workmen flatly refused to cut down the hollies in an avenue of alternating hollies and yews which had to be cleared.

A widespread superstition claims that self-sown holly should never be disturbed in a garden, for it will bring great good luck to the owner.

Around the Tamar, the ordinary holly used to be called 'Aunt Mary's Tree', for 'Aunt Mary' was one name for the holy Virgin in that area. The memory persists in the poem 'Modryb Marya' (Aunt Mary) by the Rev. R. S. Hawker. It begins:-

> *'Now the holly with her drops of blood for me,*
> *For that is our dear Aunt Mary's tree.'*

The first line of the second verse – 'Its leaves are sweet with our Saviour's Name' may contain a reference to a legend more usually associated with a particular type of variegated or 'spicketty' holly, known locally as 'holy' holly and used to deck the Christmas tree. The white spots on the leaves of this variety are supposed to be a memory of the time that our lady, whilst nursing the infant Jesus, spilt some milk onto the plant.

Medicinally, holly-leaf tea is said locally to be highly efficacious in the relief of rheumatism: fully-grown leaves should be gathered, washed clean and spread out to dry. An ounce of the dried leaf infused for ten minutes in a pint of boiling water produces a drink which should be taken, a wineglassful at a time, two or three times daily.

HONEYSUCKLE

(Lonicera periclymenum)

– Goat's Leaf
– Pride of the Evening (Hartland)
– Withywind

The Honeysuckle – the flower of Honiton – is much-loved for its sweet scent which perfumes the evening air wherever it grows. It thrives happily along hedgerows, covers old tree-stumps, trails along the woodland floor, and rambles over old fences and ruined buildings.

In parts of South Devon blossoms of one variety, Goat-Leaf Honeysuckle (Lonicera caprifolium), are still recommended for the considerable relief which they afford to sufferers from asthma: the corollas should be pulled from their calyces and an ounce infused in a pint of boiling water for ten minutes; the infusion should then be strained and added to 8oz of sugar before being bottled. The dose is one teaspoonful to be taken when attacks are troublesome.

Honeysuckle is also said to be of value as an emergency treatment for snake-bite: anyone bitten by a viper should suck the juice of the honeysuckle, and apply its leaves to the wound whilst awaiting professional aid.

HOUSELEEK
(Sempervivum tectorum)

– Zilgreen

The red flowers of the houseleek, with their mass of yellow stamens, thick stems and rosette of leaves, may be seen growing upon roofs of cottages and outhouses. It is said that this plant provides protection against fire, lightning, and evil forces: indeed, a local superstition maintains that luck will never depart from a house which has houseleeks adorning its roof!

Medicinally, its juice, mixed with cream, is said to be an excellent treatment for inflammation and skin irritations. In the seventeenth century in South Devon the plant was recommended for 'heat in the face': a small houseleek was boiled in cream with red dock roots which had first been scraped and sliced. When the mixture had become an oil, a little fenugreek was added and the whole beaten until cold.

More recently, the juice of the house-leek has been found useful in the treatment of corns and warts: the leaves should be pulled away from the central rosette, and the broken edge placed upon the corn or wart whilst the sap is gently squeezed out onto it; the treatment should be repeated night and morning.

From Tiverton comes the information that house-leeks, crushed and mixed with lard, will bring speedy relief to sufferers from broken chilblains.

IVY *(Hedera helix)*

– Ivy-drum
– Ivy-tod

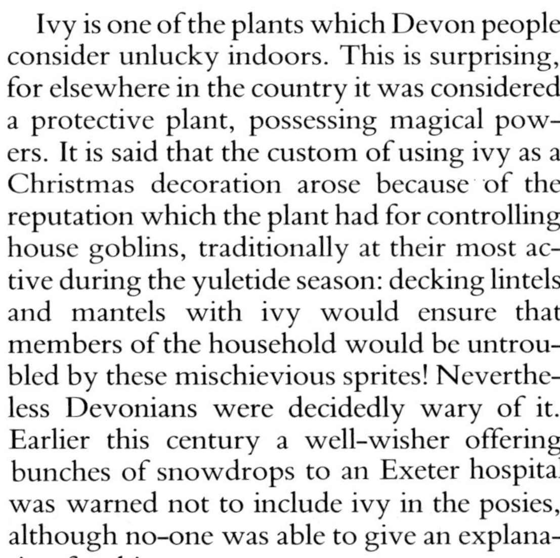

Ivy is one of the plants which Devon people consider unlucky indoors. This is surprising, for elsewhere in the country it was considered a protective plant, possessing magical powers. It is said that the custom of using ivy as a Christmas decoration arose because of the reputation which the plant had for controlling house goblins, traditionally at their most active during the yuletide season: decking lintels and mantels with ivy would ensure that members of the household would be untroubled by these mischievious sprites! Nevertheless Devonians were decidedly wary of it. Earlier this century a well-wisher offering bunches of snowdrops to an Exeter hospital was warned not to include ivy in the posies, although no-one was able to give an explanation for this strange request.

To dream of ivy, a plant which owing to its clinging nature has become symbolic of love, is encouraging, for according to an old Devonian interpretation it means that one's friendships are true.

Medicinally, it has been used in the past to treat those suffering from mumps. Both the leaves and the berries were used in an infusion which was to be taken at regular intervals. In addition, an external application was said to be very soothing, and minor burns such as sunburn could be relieved by an ointment made by boiling ivy stalks in butter, and applying this to the sore areas.

Ivy was once used to recondition black silk. The leaves were mashed and boiled in water until they had given off much of their colour. The water was then strained, and the silk rinsed in it, and then allowed to dry naturally, away from direct sunlight.

JUNIPER *(Juniperus communis)*

Juniper is one of Devon's oldest inhabitants, for there is evidence to suggest that it flourished here some 12,000 years ago. Today, it is found growing wild in certain moorland areas, where it often appears as a spreading, twisted shrub. Its foliage consists of short, blue-green, spiky needles which have a white streak along their upper surface. The berries are rounded and green at first, but deepen to purple in their second year.

This is a plant whose protective powers were paid tribute to as far back as biblical times. When Elijah was in danger of persecution by Ahab, it was said to be the juniper which preserved him; and according to legend, Mary hid herself and the infant Christ behind a juniper-bush when fleeing from Herod.

However, juniper also protects on a more mundane level, for it is a natural antiseptic. Housewives used to burn its berries and branches to prevent infection from spreading, and those in contact with contagious illness chewed juniper berries as an added precaution. In the days before refrigeration when it was difficult to prevent meat from going 'off' during hot weather, it was usual to add a few crushed berries both to enhance its flavour and to counteract any taint. Crushed berries were also added to the water in which clothes were being washed in what must have been one of the earliest 'bacterial' washing agents.

Juniper also has its medicinal uses. In the 1920s an old lady in her eighties from South Molton used to treat rheumatism with seven drops of juniper oil, clearly considering that the number '7' possessed some mystical power which would increase the efficacy of the cure. The plant has been used in the treatment of this condition for some considerable time, although it was more usual to prescribe juniper tea or wine.

A liniment, beneficial in cases of rheumatic and other types of muscular pain, used to be made by steeping 2ozs of juniper berries in a pint of olive oil for a fortnight, and was massaged into any painful areas. Backache could also be relieved by juniper oil: a drop of this was placed upon a lump of sugar, and the treatment repeated two or three times a day.

Juniper berries are still used today as a flavouring for gin.

LEMON VERBENA
(Lippia citriodora)

For many centuries, lemon verbena has been associated with love. It was considered sacred to Venus, and was traditionally strewn in bridal chambers. A sprig was often included amongst the stuffing of bridal pillows, for the sweet lemon scent was reputed to have aphrodisiac properties. A resident of Northam in the 1920s told of the belief that no-one who can make cuttings of lemon verbena grow will die unmarried; however, the lady, herself an elderly spinster added, with a twinkle in her eye: 'I don't think it's always true, because I can make it grow.'

Another local superstition maintains that no house which has lemon verbena growing in its garden can ever be damaged by storms or hail.

LILAC *(Syringa vulgaris)*

- Duck's Bills
- Laylock
- Maybushes
- Oyster (Parracombe)
- Pipe Tree
- Prince-of-Wales-Feather
- Queen's Feather

Though pretty and sweet-smelling, there is nevertheless a widespread superstition in Devon that it is unlucky to bring lilac into the house. When, in May 1939, a visitor to the widow of an old sea-captain took with her a bunch of lilacs, the widow was horrified: 'Daun't 'e bring no laylocks in 'ouze, my dear!' she exclaimed, 'They do zay it be ter'ble onlucky!' We do not know where the old lady lived, but the belief was certainly prevalent in Newton Abbot at about this period.

Several generations of royal brides have had Honiton lace incorporated into their dress or veil, and flowers were very often included in the design for this lace. When the future Queen Adalaide married King William IV, lilac was one of the flowers used to spell out her name, thus:-

Amaranth
Daphne
Eglantine
Lilac
Auricula
Ivy
Dahlia
Eglantine

MALLOW *(Malva sylvestris)*

- Bread & Cheese
- Bull's Eyes
- Cheese
- Cheese Nut
- Chucky Cheese
- Pancake Plant

The common mallow is a shrub which abounds on roadsides, waste ground and banks throughout the county. It grows to almost a metre in height, has quite large, rounded leaves at the base, and smaller, ivy-shaped leaves growing from the stem. The five-petalled, pink flowers have darker veins and appear between June and September. They are followed by round fruits which are rather like the old-fashioned, circular cheeses, hence their local name of 'cheese' or 'cheese-nut'.

Children for generations have enjoyed nibbling these 'cheeses', for they have a pleasant, nutty flavour, but they were not alone in recognising the value of the mallow as a foodstuff. Poor folk in the past frequently used the leaves of this plant as an enjoyable and nutritious vegetable.

The generic name for mallow is derived from a Greek word meaning 'soft and soothing', for like the marsh mallow it contains a type of mucus which is effective in the treatment of sores. In seventeenth century Devon the plant was one ingredient in a cure for cramp: an oil was made by boiling together mallow leaves and camomile flowers with parsley and butter or salad oil. The oil was then rubbed into the affected muscle.

For cases of running gout the oils of mallow, camomile, foxglove and dill were combined and 'worked in well before the fire with a warm hand.'

MARIGOLD
(Calendula officinalis)

- Drunkards

The old-fashioned marigold grows so happily and seeds itself so readily that it has become regarded by many gardeners as a weed. However, its attractive orange or yellow flowers, which are rather like large daisies, bloom so cheerfully for much of the year that it is a welcome addition to any cottage garden.

The Latin name *'Calendula'* pays tribute to the marigold's long flowering season, for it suggests that it blossoms on the calends (first) of every month.

It is also said to be a plant which 'follows the sun', for as well as shutting its petals at dusk, it will even turn its face during the day

in order to allow the sun to shine directly upon it. The Devon poet, William Browne, remarked on this in *'Britannia Pastorals' Book III)*:-

'So shuts the marigold her leaves
At the departure of the sun;
So from the honeysuckle sheaves
The bee goes when the day is done.'

And Robert Herrick made a similar observation in his 'Hesperides':-

'Give way, and be ye ravisht by the sun,
(And hang the head when as the act is done)
Spread as he spreads: wax less as he do's wane;
And as he shuts, close up to maids again.'

Somewhat suprisingly, this little flower was once deemed to be the badge of jealousy. According to Robert Herrick:-

'Jealous girls these sometimes were,
While they lived, or lasted here:
Turned to flowers, still they be
Yellow, marked for jealousy.'

It also has a strange association with drunkenness, as its local name of 'drunkards' suggests. It used to be believed that anyone who picked a marigold, or even looked at one too closely, would inevitably turn to drink!

More happily, it is said to be very fortunate to dream of this flower, for according to a Devonian interpretation, such a dream augurs wealth, prosperity, and a rich and happy marriage.

Marigolds have been used medicinally for many years. In the 1880s an infusion made from their petals was recommended in Exmouth for anyone who wished to avoid contracting the measles; it was thought to be equally good for those actually suffering from the disease.

People afflicted with rheumatism have also gained considerable relief from drinking such an infusion three or four times a day. It was made by steeping an ounce of flowers in a pint of boiling water, and allowing the mixture to brew.

The leaves are believed to possess antiseptic and anti-inflammatory properties, so were often used to treat skin sores and cuts. One old cure advises that they should first be chewed, and then bound over the sore area.

Anyone returning home with aching feet might care to try bathing them in water which has a cupful of marigold leaves added to it, for this is said to be extremely soothing.

MARJORAM *(Origanum spp.)*

The name 'Origanum' is derived from two Greek words meaning 'mountain joy', and in ancient times marjoram was regarded as a symbol of happiness. In Devon it was seen as having more practical benefits, for a local superstition maintains that if marjoram and wild thyme are laid by milk in a dairy, this will prevent it from being 'turned' by thunder.

Marjoram has also been used to dye wool purple, and because of its pleasant scent was included in pot pourris and furniture polish. It has medicinal use as well, for sweet marjoram used to be administered in cases of dropsy. From Chudleigh comes the information that it was also given to sufferers from thrombosis: the leaves were powdered and mixed with honey, and 'as much as will lie on the top of a knife' given every morning.

MARSH MALLOW

(Althaea officinalis)

As its name suggests, Marsh Mallow is a plant which favours wet areas, most often found along river-banks and streams. Like the mallow, its root is rich in a mucus which has been found to have great soothing and healing properties when applied to inflamed sores; its ability to prevent gangrene from setting in has led to its becoming known as the 'Mortification Root'.

An elderly gentleman from Exeter recommends the following treatment for really stubborn bruises and blistered heels which seem to be becoming infected: the marsh mallow should be boiled in water and the infected area bathed with the liquor; a plaster should then be made of the leaves, and this bound onto the wound. The procedure should be repeated for several days until the condition heals completely.

The marsh mallow has been found useful, too, in the prevention and treatment of animal disease: many local farmers allowed it to flourish on their farms since cattle both enjoy it and derive benefit from it. The pulped leaves and blossoms were applied warm to make a poultice for swellings and external injuries or skin complaints; and the roots boiled and sweetened with honey were found to be useful in the treatment of internal inflammations.

In past times mothers of teething babies knew the value of the marsh mallow root when their infants were fretful: the root relieved the soreness of the gums and helped to ease the cutting of teeth.

MEADOWSWEET

(Spiraea (Fillipendula) ulmaria)

- Bridewort
- Coutship and Matrimony
- Goat's Beard
- Honey Flower
- Queen of the Meadow
- Summer's Farewell

Meadowsweet is a highly fragrant plant growing in wet areas such as the banks of rivers, streams or canals, or in damp meadows or woods. It was once traditionally used as a wedding flower, for since its sweet fragrance is strongest when crushed, it was customary to strew the bridal path with 'Bridewort'. The plant has two distinct fragrances: the leaves have a pleasant cucumbery taste and smell; the flowers, a sweet almond-like scent. The combination of the two caused the plant to become nick-named 'Courtship and Matrimony', the romantic smell of the flowers being succeeded by the appetising smell of the leaves!

The sap of meadowsweet contains salicin, an ingredient of aspirin, so it is not surprising to find that the plant has a history of use in treating sore throats and eyes. An Exeter man remembers being sent to gather it from the banks of the canal during the early part of the century so that his mother could use it for this purpose. The flowers were infused in boiling water and the liquid either drunk, in the case of sore throats, or cooled, strained well and used to bathe eyes. It was said to be excellent for relieving burning and itching in the eye.

Meadowsweet tea is also excellent for anyone feeling generally 'under the weather', and makes a pleasant drink when sweetened with honey: the flowers and leaves should be boiled in water for about ten minutes. The same brew is also said to be very good for anyone suffering from a headache.

MISTLETOE *(Viscum album)*

Popular plant of the Christmas season, Mistletoe is shrouded in superstition: an old tradition maintains that the Cross on Calvary was carved from the mistletoe, which up until that time had been a fine forest tree. Following this shameful deed, however, it was condemned to be a parasite with no life of its own, able to grow only on such trees as will tolerate its presence 'an t'isn't extra many as yu du know.'

The Druids ascribed to it a divine origin, and since they considered that it had the power to effect miraculous cures, they bestowed upon it the name 'curer of all ills'. Both the trees on which the mistletoe grew, and the birds visiting it, were considered by the Druids to be sacred–the birds being seen as messengers of the gods. And if the mistletoe had to be cut for use in pagan ritual, great ceremony accompanied the act, which was performed with a golden sickle.

It is said that the Druids put a curse upon the County of Devon, and forbade the mistletoe to grow here, and a curious story survives from the end of the last century; it concerns an orchard half in Devon and half in Somerset. Mistletoe apparently flourished on the Somerset apple-trees, but was completely absent from those on the Devon side of the border, despite repeated attempts to cultivate it!

In parts of North Devon, mistletoe was regarded as so unlucky that farmers were forbidden to grow it in their orchards. According to a servant-girl from Torquay in the 1920s, its presence was essential to the health of the apple-trees because 'Mistletoe is the poison of the apple-tree; it comes up out of the roots. That is why, when there are many apples together, they don't grow well unless there's mistletoe on them.'

One should nevertheless be wary about planting this parasite, for a Newton Abbot superstition holds that if you do so and it grows, your daughters will never marry!

Everyone knows of the custom of 'kissing under the mistletoe' at Christmas, but many people wrongly take down the plant on Twelfth Night together with the rest of the Christmas decorations, mindful perhaps of the old Devon warning that:-

'If so the superstitious find
One tiny branch just left behind,
Look! for every leaf there may be
So many goblins shall plague thee!'

MOONWORT *(Botrychium lunaria)*

- Unshoe-the-horse

Local superstition maintains that this plant is endowed with the miraculous ability to unlock any door, and its country name hints at an even stranger power which it is supposed to possess: as early as the seventeenth century the herbalist Nicholas Culpepper wrote of an incident which took place on White Down, near Tiverton. Apparently thirty horse-shoes had been pulled off the Earl of Essex's horses as they galloped over the moonwort-covered Down, even though many of these shoes had been but newly applied!

MOUNTAIN ASH

(Sorbus (Pyrus) aucuparia)

- Care (Ashwater)
- Kear (Sutcombe)
- Rowan
- Quickbeam (Ashwater)
- Twick-bine
- Witch-beam

For many centuries mountain ash has been considered a tree of protection, and Devonians believed that hanging a branch of it over their doors would ensure that no witch would be able to harm the occupants of the house – hence the local name of 'care'. A resident of Dartmouth still keeps a stick of rowan outside her cottage, primarily to keep out evil, but also to cure small ailments: recently afflicted with eczema on her face, she rubbed the stick over the sores and they soon cleared up.

In Torrington in the 1880s it was customary to hang mountain ash around the necks of sick animals since this was supposed to prevent them from growing any worse; and it was said that a horse struck with a switch from this tree would never grow fat. However, forty years later in Hartland it was considered most unlucky to hit an animal with a rowan stick, for it was held that the animal in question would be sure to develop weals upon its body.

When carving a cradle, country carpenters believed in incorporating mountain ash, for it was thought that a baby laid in such a cot would be protected from all harm. Local fishermen, too, had faith in the tree's talismanic properties, and often wore an amulet fashioned from it to ensure that no ill could befall them at sea. And in the dairy it was said that the presence of rowan was sufficient to prevent milk from curdling.

MUGWORT (*Artemesia vulgaris*)

– St. John's Wort
– Wil(d) Wormuth

A member of the wormwood family, mugwort has been nick-named 'St. John's Wort' because it was believed that John the Baptist wore a girdle of it during his time in the wilderness. This is remotely possible, because it was traditionally worn about the person to repel flies. But the association could have been deliberately made by the Church to mask mugwort's centuries-old links with sorcery, especially as it had particular associations with Midsummer's Eve, which occurs at almost the same time as the Feast of St. John. On this most magical day in the calendar the plant's roots are reputed to develop a strange 'coal' underneath them, and it is said that anyone who digs this substance up and keeps it will be protected from diverse afflictions ranging from boils to pestilence to lightning!

Mugwort is supposed to have another curious property: if placed in the shoes as a kind of 'inner-sole' it will prevent weariness on the part of long-distance walkers.

Devon women found that sachets of Mugwort placed among linen and clothes in storage kept them from being eaten by moths.

Medicinally, this was one of the plants used in the past to dissolve the stone: an early nineteenth century remedy from North Devon recommends that mugwort be prepared and eaten as common garden 'greens'.

MYRTLE (*Myrtus communis*)

There exists in Devon an old belief that no woman who is able to grow myrtle will ever die unmarried. On the other hand, if a farmer is unfortunate enough to have one of his myrtle-bushes die, then among the misfortunes he may expect will be a 'removal'.

Although it is quite difficult to grow flowering myrtle, it is said to be one of the luckiest plants to have in one's garden. Those wishing to succeed in making it flower should, when 'setting the slip' (ie planting the cutting), 'spread the tail of their dress and look proud'!

Robert Herrick expressed the widely held belief that myrtle is a symbol of love in his poem 'The Dream':-

'Me thought (last night) love in an anger came,
And brought a rod, so whipt me with the same:
Myrtle the twigs were, merely to imply,
Love strikes, but 'tis with gentle cruelty.'

NETTLE (*Urtica dioica*)

– Hidgy-Pidgy
– Hoky-Poky
– Sting-Nittle
– Deave-Nittle } Dead Nettle
– White Archangels }

It is in poorer rural areas that people have come to recognise the true worth of the stinging-nettle, for the plant has many uses: it is said to be as good as flax for making cloth, which it can also dye – green if the boiled leaves are used, or yellow if the roots are boiled with either salt or alum.

Nettles have also been an important source of food, for nettle-tops, very lightly boiled, are excellent to eat as 'greens', and said to be high in protein. A sovereign recipe for 'keeping away illness' which comes from Stockleigh Pomeroy has nettles among its principal ingredients, the others being dandelion-leaves and watercress; infused together and drunk regularly they will apparently combine to maintain the partaker in excellent health.

In Chudleigh, in the seventeenth century, red nettles and salt, boiled together, were said to be effective in the treatment of bruises; the two were made into a compress which was bound fast to the bruise and changed at regular intervals. For cuts, nettle-tops could be bruised and applied to the injury.

In Tiverton, before the last war, nettles were thought to be efficacious in cases of pleurisy. They were boiled in a saucepan for 15 minutes, and ½–1 teaspoon of the decoction given to the patient. At the same time, scalding nettle-leaves were made into a poultice which, when cool, was put onto flannel over the painful area and covered with oilcloth. Someone suffering from asthma, or having difficulty in breathing, might have been placed in a room where nettles were being burnt. Or, if his illness was shingles, he might have been given nettle-tea.

Nettles were also believed to be useful in the relief of rheumatism: one suggestion from Moretonhampstead was that the sufferer should drink an infusion made from this plant, whilst a gentleman from Totnes perpetuates a very old country method of treating the complaint by stinging himself daily with nettles; it seems that the formic acid in the stings probably has a beneficial effect upon the condition.

Nettle-juice is supposed to be soothing if applied to bee-stings, but the traditional cure for the stings of the nettles themselves is the dock-leaf; it used to be said that near to every clump of nettles, nature in her bounty had planted a dock, which if rubbed over the sting brings speedy relief. Alternatively, sage, mint, rue, plantain and elder are also supposed to be effective.

The nettle features in a strange and ancient charm for bad eyes, known in North Devon during the latter half of the last century. A small boy from the village of Berrynarbor was afflicted with bad eyes, and his parents were told that he could be cured by a woman who had never seen her father blowing into his eyes through a hole in a nettle-leaf first thing in the morning, before she had put her hand to anything for the day. The child's father took him every morning for nine days to such a person at Ilfracombe, and his eyes recovered completely! Apparently, in the case of a girl sufferer, she must be taken to a man who had never seen his mother.

In parts of Devon, among them Bovey-Tracey, Torquay, North Tawton and Tiverton, the 3rd May used to be celebrated as sting-nittle day! although one report has it on 1st May instead. No-one knows the origin of the custom, whereby children would arm themselves with bunches of nettles and go around beating one another with them. One suggestion is that it is a commemoration of the introduction of nettles into England by the Romans, who seem to have used them to stimulate the circulation in their limbs in an effort to withstand the cold and damp of our British winter. A Tiverton gentleman recalls that during his childhood in the late 1950s he used to hold the bunch of nettles behind his back and ask innocently 'Do you know what day it is?'. If the answer was 'No', the stinging nettles would be promptly swung into action,

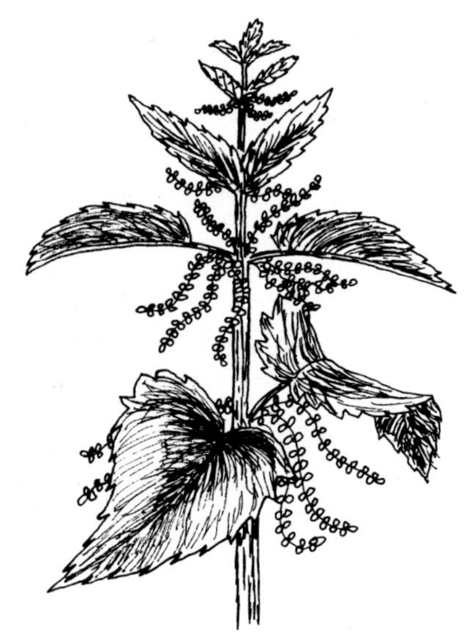

with the cry 'sting-nittle day!' Twenty years earlier his mother, who was also from Tiverton, would decorate the breakfast table with a bunch of nettles on the appointed day, while her mother's back was turned. In justification for any nefarious actions involving the use of nettles on this day, children would merely chant:

'First of May is "May-Doll" Day,
Second of May is Kissing Day,
Third of May is Sting-Nittle Day!'

Nettle also had their uses in the brewing industry, for they were found to be very useful in making emergency repairs to the casks. Nettle-juice was applied to any small cracks, and was said to seal them quite effectively.

Anyone who allows a clump of nettles to flourish in a corner of their garden will not only be able to enjoy their medicinal benefits but hopefully will also be rewarded by the sight of two British butterflies who are entirely dependent upon this plant for their survival. Both the Peacock and the Small Tortoiseshell lay their eggs only upon nettle leaves, and the black caterpillar relies upon them for its food.

NUTMEG *(Myristica fragrans)*

Nutmeg is the seed of the tropical, evergreen tree which also gives us mace. It has been a popular spice for quite some time, and was the ingredient of an old Devon charm for 'pinsoles' (boils) or abscesses. This charm was practised in Torrington in the 1880s and was still being used in North Bovey in the 1950s, and involves the sufferer being given a nutmeg by a person of the opposite sex. The nutmeg was placed in the pocket and nibbled periodically: by the time that it had gone completely the boils too would have vanished.

Anyone wishing to try this charm should proceed cautiously, however, for nutmeg has hallucinogenic properties similar to those of marijuana, and it is said that death can result from eating as few as two!

OAK *(Quercus robur)*

– Chitjack
– Cups and Saucers
– Oak-mas

The mighty oak is one of the most popular and majestic trees of the English countryside, and first came to our region some seven thousand years ago. Until man began to clear the ground for cultivation, vast oak forests covered much of Devon, and relics of these may still be found on certain parts of the Moor. Many of our finest trees, however, were probably planted in Elizabethan times, when oak was very widely used for making furniture, and also in shipbuilding and housing. Its popularity was due to its strength, durability and great beauty.

Oak trees can attain vast ages, some of the oldest in Devon probably being well over 500 years old, and occurring as stunted, twisted specimens in places such as Wistman's Wood. However, strange looking oaks are not confined to these old forests, where poor soils and scything winds are accountable for their deformities. Isolated deformed trees occur in various areas, and have given rise to some quite fascinating legends. One of the best known is that of the 'Twisty-Tree' of Ide, a mighty oak which stood at the side of the road on the approach to the village, and was remarkable in that the bark of its trunk had become twisted in corkscrew fashion. Various explanations have been advanced for this strange malformation: one, dating from the middle of the last century, maintains that the village of Ide was once haunted by a troublesome sprite who turned milk and beer sour, kept butter from coming and dough from rising, frightened maidens in the dark and set neighbours quarrelling, so that Ide had become almost uninhabitable. The residents, in desperation, appealed to an Oxford scholar who laid the ghost in the tree. All discomforts ceased immediately, but the spirit so hated his prison that he twisted incessantly inside it in an effort to regain his freedom. In course of time, the tree arrived at its twisted appearance.

Also from Ide comes the story of 'Grandfather's Oak', a twisted tree standing at the foot of the hill which leads into Ide from Littlejohn Cross. It is possible that this and the 'twisty-tree' may be one and the same. In the 1930s it was the custom for members of the Pitman family to salute the tree by raising their hats to it whenever they passed by. How, when or why this custom arose no-one knows: one theory is that the 'grandfather' after whom the tree is named was Samuel Pitman (1749-1788) and that he may have planted the tree; by saluting it his descendants are therefore honouring the memory of an ancestor. Another theory concerns 'The Major' (James Pitman 1779-1848): some say that his spirit is confined within it; others, that the tree twisted on the night that he died. The oak has also been associated with a suicide.

From Bridestowe we hear of the legend of the 'Ghost-Tree', an ancient and blasted oak standing at the corner of a lane through which passes Lady Howard's spectral procession. This procession consists of a coach of bones drawn by headless horses and preceeded by a one-eyed, large black hound, and is said to

carry Lady Howard each night from her former home in Tavistock to Okehampton Castle. The tree acquired its name because it was a landmark on this route, and owing to its eerie associations a woodsman employed by a former owner of the land on which it stands desired to cut it down. However, the owner, one Shilston Calmady-Hamlyn, refused to give his permission, and by way of a compliment to him the 'Ghost Tree' was renamed 'Shilston's Oak'.

Another legend has given rise to the annual celebration of Oak-Apple Day. This takes place on 29th May, and commemorates the escape of the future King Charles II after the battle of Worcester in 1651; he evaded capture by the Roundheads by hiding in an oak tree. The date itself was not that of the escape, but rather of Charles's entry into London after the Restoration in 1660; it was also the monarch's birthday. The celebration of Oak-Apple day has declined in recent years, although in the 1970s the village of Membury continued to hoist an oak bough to the top of the church tower on 29th May. In former times, however, people would traditionally wear oak-leaves and oak-apples on this day, and children would arm themselves with bunches of stinging-nettles with which to beat anyone not wearing the decoration. This custom was observed in Torquay in 1880, and was also current in Ilsington. Sixty years later the residents of Tedburn St. Mary continued to wear the leaves on Oak-Apple Day as a protection not against being flogged by nettles, but rather against being pinched! There was a slight variation, however; here, oak leaves were worn in the morning, ash in the afternoon.

Acorns, known locally as 'cups and saucers', are the fruits of the oak, and it used to be quite common at one time for young women to carry one about with them at all times, for doing so was supposed to be a sure way of preserving their youthful good looks. They were also widely used by country lads and lasses to learn whether or not their love would endure. Two acorns were taken, and one given the name of the boy, the other the name of the girl. They were then placed side-by-side in a bowl of water, and if they floated towards one another, marriage between the two parties was said to be certain. If the acorns drifted apart, however, then either one of them would prove faithless, or else something would occur to prevent the marriage from taking place.

The knobs attached to the cords of window blinds are often shaped like an acorn: this is because the oak-tree was once dedicated to Thor, the God of Thunder, and as a result it is widely believed that neither the tree itself nor its fruit can ever be struck by a thunder-bolt. If an acorn is hung at the window, it naturally follows that the house must be protected as well. Some variations of the superstition maintain that this protection will only be afforded to the righteous.

The oak's associations with magic do not end there for even today there are carpenters who believe that oak should be joined with wooden pegs rather than nails. On the other hand, a nail driven into an oak trunk is reputed to be an instant cure for toothache. And anyone owning a sickly pear or apple tree which refuses to bear fruit might care to heed the advice of an old gardener from Stockleigh Pomeroy; he maintained that a green oak peg driven into a hole which has been bored into the trunk of the fruit tree will give it a new lease of life. It seems very likely that behind such superstitions lies a memory of the time when the oak was the sacred tree of the Druids, who held it in very high esteem.

When the gall-fly attacks an oak-tree, galls which are known as 'oak-apples' frequently form. A seventeenth century remedy for warts from Chudleigh recommends that these should be pounded and tempered with tart vinegar, and the resultant mixture applied to the wart. However, local superstition warns that anyone who finds a worm in an oak-apple is doomed to poverty; the finding of a spider signifies instead that the finder will become ill.

ONION

– Scallions }
– Chipples } – Spring Onions

It is said that to dream of eating onions is extremely fortunate, for it signifies that the dreamer can expect to find a great deal of money in the very near future. Nevertheless, associations with this vegetable are not always so happy, for at the beginning of the century the residents of Ashburton were convinced that if onion skins were burnt in the house of anyone who kept livestock, then that person's mares would be incapable of producing live colts, and his sheep would be stricken by misfortune.

These skins, however, were used by country folk as indicators of the coming weather prospects. A well-known rhyme states that:

> *'If the onion skins are very thin*
> *Then a mild winter is coming in;*
> *But if the onion skins are thick and tough*
> *Then the coming winter will be cold and rough'.*

The power of this vegetable to soak up smells and germs has long been exploited: those working among strong fumes, such as dyers and painters, used to place chopped raw onions in the room in which they were working. Similarly, it was an ancient practice to place a saucer containing a raw onion-half in any room where infection was present, for it was thought that this would absorb the infection and prevent it from spreading.

In more romantic vein, young girls in Devon used onions to discover which of their suitors was the most faithful. An onion would be taken for each suitor, and his initials scratched upon it with a needle: the onions would then be placed in a dark cupboard, and the first to sprout would indicate the truest love. If a girl places an onion under her pillow on St. Thomas's Eve she will dream of her future husband.

As well as being a delicious flavouring for soups and stews, onions are good heart strengtheners, and of benefit in treating and preventing a number of ills. On the principle of the Doctrine of Signatures, because they cause the eyes to water when cut it was concluded that they must be good for colds. Thus country folk believed that including plenty of onions in their diet would keep them free from winter chills and maintain them in good health throughout the year. A specific Devon remedy for colds and flu was a type of onion soup, made from thickly chopped onions cooked in milk.

Should a cold threaten, it might be stopped from developing by sucking raw onion. If not caught in time, relief could be gained by pouring runny honey thickly over chopped onion, covering it and leaving it overnight: the next morning a syrup would have formed which could be taken by the spoonful. The addition of a little horseradish to the syrup would greatly benefit sufferers from catarrh.

Onions were used in the treatment of certain other specific conditions: red onions, mixed with horsemint, were thought to be able to 'dissolve the stone', according to an early nineteenth century remedy from North Devon. The juice was extracted from both ingredients (but only red onions would be effective in this cure) and a spoonful administered night and morning.

Used in Teignbridge in the late seventeenth century to treat deafness, an onion was cored, and oils of bays, frankincense and aquavitae placed into the cavity: the whole was then roasted in the embers of the fire, and eventually wrung through a fine cloth. The liquid was collected, and a small drop placed in the ear until it had penetrated: the treatment was repeated until the hearing improved, probably as a result of the softening and dispersion of accumulated wax. The use of warm onion in cases of earache is still recommended today.

Its virtues did not end there, however. Many Devonians persist in rubbing raw onion over bee-stings, for they claim that this affords them swift relief. Chilblains, too, are said to benefit from being covered with a poultice made from pounded onions and salt.

The onion has yet one more place in Devon folk history. In 1072 AD, the city of Exeter mourned the death of its Bishop, Leofric. Among his bequests was an anthology of Anglo-Saxon poetry, included in which was this riddle:-

'I'm an odd creature, for I satisfy women
a service to the neighbours. Nobody suffers
at my hands except my killer,
I grow very tall, erect in a bed,
I'm hairy below. From time to time
a beautiful maiden, the brave daughter
of some peasant dares to grasp me,
squeezes my ruddy skin, robs me of my top
and puts me in the larder.
At once that maiden
with plaited tresses who has imprisoned me
recalls our meeting. Her eye moistens'.

The answer to the riddle is, of course, an onion!

PANSY *(Viola tricolor)*

– Kiss-me-at-the-garden-gate
– Kiss-me-love
– Kiss-me-quick
– Old Maid's Last Friend
– Heartsease

The name 'Pansy' is derived from the French word 'pensees' meaning 'thoughts', and the plant is frequently associated with love, as its quaint local names suggest. Herrick knew of this association and wrote the following poem to describe how the flower came into being:-

'Frolick virgins once there were
Ever loving, ever there
Being there, their ends denied,
Ran for sweethearts mad, and died.
Love, in pity of their tears,
And their loss in blooming years,
For their restless here-spent hours
Gave them heart's ease, turned to flowers'.

It used to be thought that if pansies were placed upon the eyes of a sleeper, that person would be compelled to fall in love with the first person he or she saw upon awakening. Pansy-juice squeezed into the eyes whilst asleep was rumoured to have the same effect.

One of the flower's best-known names is 'heartsease', for it is supposed to ease the heart of any lover whose sentiments are not returned. Unrequited in love, Robert Herrick turned to it for comfort in another of his poems, entitled 'To Pansies':-

'Ah, cruel love, must I endure
Thy many scorns, and find no cure?
Say, are thy medicines made to be
Helps to all others, but to me?
I'll leave thee and to pansies come;
Comforts you'll afford me some:
You can ease my heart, and do
What Love co'd ne'er be brought unto'.

PARSLEY *(Petroselium sativum)*

Devonians have long considered Parsley to be a plant of evil omen, and a host of superstitions have grown up around it, among them a belief that it is most unlucky either to plant or transplant the herb. A paper read before the Devon & Exeter Gardeners' Association in 1897, whilst giving excellent practical advice on the cultivation of parsley, allowed itself to lapse into folklore by stating that 'it is one of the longest seeds to lie in the ground before germinating; it has been said to go to the Devil and back nine times before coming up. And many people have a great objection to planting parsley, saying that if you do so there will be sure to be a death in the family within twelve months'.

Associations between this plant and the Devil are strong. In Northam it was believed that parsley-seed went to the Devil before sprouting, but in this instance only three times. And in Morchard Bishop at the end of the last century it was said that the failure of parsley to grow in any location was a sign of Satan's continued presence there, although to set it in the ground was to court misfortune, sickness and death.

To counteract these evil associations several measures were taken, all designed to weaken the demonic hold on the plant. In Hartland it was held that parsley should only be sown by a woman; in Newton Abbot and Tavistock, only when the church bells were ringing; and the inhabitants of Shillingford and Totnes were amongst those who prefer to sow the herb on Good Friday – one way of ensuring that there will be an adequate supply for the whole year.

Coal-dust was also thought to assist germination. Earlier this century a Captain Smith of the Priory, Totnes, who had regularly sown parsley without success, followed the advice of his jobbing gardener and mixed the seed with coal-dust prior to sowing: he was rewarded with a flourishing crop!

In 1940 a passer-by witnessed a curious Devon practice when he perceived a young woman planting parsley with a spoon. When challenged, she explained that she did this to prevent the electricity of the body from running out! Her father voiced another very strong superstition, widespread throughout the county, when he stated that he would not transplant parsley for £100, a sizeable sum in the 1940s. In Crediton such an action was expected to result in the grave misfortune, sickness or death of one of the household, whilst in the 1870s the clerk of a Devon parish bordering on Morwenstow was said to have been bed-ridden 'ever since the parsley mores were moved'. Another man said he would rather leave the employ of the master he had served for forty years than transplant parsley to fill a bed.

The success or failure of this herb to grow is also said to be an indication of who is the true head of the household. An old Devonian saying maintains that 'Where Missus is Maister parsley won't grow', although in Clovelly they believe the reverse and where the plant grows well the woman is boss!

If one has a flourishing crop and wishes to share it with a friend, one should go about this very carefully, for another local superstition informs us that anyone who gives parsley away is giving his luck away with it! The problem can best be resolved by allowing one's friend to 'steal' the herb, for luck will not leave with stolen parsley.

But, if parsley is infamous for bad luck, its medicinal value has long been recognised. Freshly picked, and laid upon the forehead, it is said to be excellent for headaches, and as early as the seventeenth century it was being used in the Chudleigh area to treat urinary disorders: the juice, extracted and drunk in white wine or ale, was supposed to relieve renal colic and 'strangury' (painful and difficult discharge of urine), and to dissolve kidney-stones.

In Tiverton in the early part of this century parsley and groundsel were combined in the treatment of water-stoppage in both humans and animals: a double-handful of each was boiled in water and then strained and drunk, the dose being a pint for a man, and four for an animal.

Parsley tea was still being administered in North Devon in the 1950s in cases of retention of urine following childbirth, particularly in nervous patients. About a handful of ordinary garden parsley was put into a pint of cold water and boiled down to a cupful. The treatment, which was generally though not invariably successful, usually worked in about half-an-hour, although with particularly nervous women it sometimes had to be repeated 2–4 times. No records exist to indicate that this practice was known outside Devon.

Parsley has another association with childbirth, albeit a much less savoury one. Despite the local saying that 'to sow parsley is to sow babies', the herb was used to achieve quite the opposite effect. Young girls who found themselves with unwanted pregnancies would try to induce an abortion by eating large quantities of parsley.

Parsley is also said to be useful in treating piles (haemorrhoids). Its seeds, chewed, are especially good for anyone with a weak head for alcohol, since they are supposed to increase one's level of tolerance for it. Stewed parsley is recommended as an excellent remedy for indigestion, and the water in which it has been stewed may be massaged into the scalp to cure dandruff. Additionally, it is a natural deodorant, and if chewed for a few minutes after eating garlic will clear the breath completely.

PENNYROYAL *(Mentha pulegium)*

- Organs
- Pudding Grass

Posies of Pennyroyal – a member of the mint family –were frequently kept in Devon cottages to keep them free of fleas and other infestations, as the name 'pulegium' –derived from the Latin word for a flea – suggests. In former times it was customary to place the flower in churches as well, in order to rid them of these unpleasant parasites! Rats were also said to be deterred by the scent of pennyroyal, and ants will shun any area where it has been placed.

Locally, the plant used to be known as 'organs', and a tea made from it was traditionally taken out to the harvesters in the fields. As well as being very refreshing, it proved to be an excellent 'pick-me-up', able to put renewed energy into the workers. Sailors, too, valued this herb and used it to sweeten their drinking water while they were away at sea.

Others who might benefit from an infusion of pennyroyal are those who habitually suffer from cramp. The infusion may be made by pouring a pint of boiling water over an ounce of the dried herb (or a little more if fresh pennyroyal is used), and allowing this to brew for about five minutes.

Pennyroyal is also known in Devon as 'pudding-grass' – a reference to the fact that it was one of the main ingredients of a type of stuffing known as a 'pudding'.

PENNY-WORT

(Hydrocotyle vulgaris/Umbilicus rupestris)

- Devil's Candlestick
- Dimplewort
- Halfpennies and Pennies
- Iceplant
- Kidneywort
- Knipple-leaves
- Navelwort
- Nipple
- Penny cakes/caps/leaves/plates

There are two kinds of pennywort, marsh (Hydrocotyle vulgaris) and wall (Umbilicus rupestis), the latter being the most common in Devon. It is a familiar sight along the hedgerows of the country, but it is most noticeable when it juts out from crevices in walls or bare rock, for it seems amazing that it could have gained a foothold in such poor soil conditions. However, the specific name 'rupestris' means 'a rock-growing plant' so wall pennywort is obviously well suited to such situations.

The fleshy leaves of the pennywort are shaped like small saucers with a dimple in their centre where they are joined to the stalks–hence such local names as 'dimplewort' or 'navelwort'. They are about the size of an old penny, which accounts for the plant being known as 'pennywort', and also explains such nicknames as 'moneypennies' and 'pennycakes' etc.

Locally, pennywort has been used as a cure for chilblains, and also for tenderness of the breasts. The soft skin from the underneath of the leaves was massaged gently over the affected parts, and was said to afford considerable relief. A report from Tiverton in the 1940s reads as follows:-

> *'Margaret, aged five, was 'crunting' because of the chilblains, and the butcher said to her mother; 'Get some penny-worts, missus, the finest thing in the world for chilblains. There's a fine skin on those leaves underneath, and you pull that off, and there's soft stuff like a bean inside and you put that on the chilblain. Women used to put the leaf on sore breasts, too.'*

An old belief maintains that, when applied to a wound, one side of the penny-wort draws, and the other side heals.

PERIWINKLE

(Vinca major or Vinca minor)

- Bachelor's Button (Moretonhampstead)
- Blue bell
- Blue betsy
- Blue star
- Merry-goes
- Pennywrinkle
- Prinkle

Long regarded as a symbol of friendship and loyalty, periwinkle was one of the ingredients of old-fashioned love potions. It used to be believed that if lovers chewed its leaves, the bond of love between them would be strengthened.

This flower was one of those known as 'bachelor's button', as it was used in love-divination. One form of this was for a girl to pick a number of periwinkle buds and give one to each of her suitors to wear in his button-hole: she would then look to see which flower developed into the finest bloom and choose its wearer as her true love.

Alternatively, a lover who was unsure whether or not his affection was returned would pick a 'bachelor's button' and place it in his pocket. If it kept its colour his suit would be successful, but if the flower faded, so too would his love affair.

Medicinally, periwinkle is supposed to be a good general tonic if an ounce of the leaves, fresh or dried, is infused in a pint of boiling water, and a wineglassful of the infusion taken night and morning. The leaves are believed to possess a certain sedative property, and when chewed are supposed to calm nervous disorders and hysteria; people troubled by nightmares might gain relief by eating boiled periwinkle leaves.

Another virtue of chewed periwinkle leaves is the power to stop nose-bleeds, although a seventeenth century herbalist declared that Christians could be cured of the same condition if they made periwinkles into a garland and hung them around their necks.

Winding the stems, however, around any part of the body which is regularly afflicted by cramp, is said to ensure that repeat attacks will never occur.

PLANTAIN *(Plantago spp.)*

- Hard-Heads
- Heads and Tails
- Ponies' Tails

} Greater Plantain (Plantago major)

- Niggers' Heads – Hoary Plantain (Plantago media)

- Chimney Sweepers
- Cock-grass
- Fathers and Mothers
- Fighting-Cocks
- French and English Soldiers
- Knobby-heads
- Scat
- Soldiers – Ribwort Plantain (Plantago lanceolata)

There are several varieties of plantain, easily recognisable by their upright stems bearing dark, dense flower-heads, often with 'whiskers' of whitish sepals. All types flower during the summer months, and may be found in meadows and waste-land, or along grassy-verges, paths and lawns.

The word 'Plantain' is derived from the Latin 'planta', meaning the sole of the foot, and in the colonies the flower became nicknamed 'white man's foot', because settlers spread it wherever they went, probably carrying the seed on the soles of their shoes.

Locally, ribwort plantain is known as 'soldiers' or 'fighting cocks', because generations of children have enjoyed using them in a game which is very similar to 'conkers'. Two children each choose a plantain flower and pick it close to the root: they then take it in turns to hit one another's plant with a view to slicing off the opponent's flower-head. The winner is the one whose plantain survives the longest.

Other local names such as 'knobby-heads' or 'ponies tails' describe well the plant's appearance, as does 'chimney-sweepers' for the flowers do resemble a sweep's brush.

Medicinally, plantain has the reputation in Devon of being able to cure, or at least prevent blood-poisoning, merely by the rubbing of the back of a leaf over the inflamed area. It was one of the ingredients in a very highly-esteemed salve which an Exeter ointment-maker made right up to her death at the beginning of the century: the salve contained plantain leaves, southernwood, blackcurrant leaves, elder buds, parsley and angelica, all the ingredients being chopped, pounded and simmered together with clarified butter. This ointment was held to be very useful in the treatment of burns or rawness of the skin.

Three hundred years ago in Chudleigh, plantain was also used to cure 'a flux': the roots and leaves were bruised, strained and made into a cake which was eaten hot before food in the morning.

Plantain leaves have also been found effective in the treatment of stings, whether from nettles, bees, wasps or mosquitoes. The fresh leaves should be bruised slightly and rubbed gently onto the affected part, and immediate relief should be felt. The same treatment is recommended for those afflicted with piles.

PRIMROSE

(Primula vulgaris)

– Butter Rose
– Key Flower
– Lent Rose (Stockland)
– Pimrose
– Purmrose

The sight of primroses blossoming in the early Spring is a welcome one indeed! The delicate, pale yellow flowers with their orange-veined throat smother the banks and woodlands.

The name 'primrose' is derived from the Latin 'prima rosa', meaning 'first rose', in acknowledgement of the fact that it is one of the first flowers to bloom at the end of the winter, hence why Robert Herrick referred to it as the 'sweet infanta of the year'.

'Aske me why I send you here
This sweet infanta of the yeere?
Aske me why I send to you
This primrose, thus bepearl'd with dew?
I will whisper to your eares,
The sweets of love are mixt with tears.

Ask me why this flower do's show
So yellow-green, and sickly too?
Ask me why the stalk is weak
And bending, (yet it doth not break?)
I will answer, these discover
What fainting hopes are in a lover.'

Locally, the primrose was one of the flowers known as a 'key-flower'; this dates back to the ancient superstition that such a flower, if pressed against a rock behind which hidden treasure was believed to be located, would cause the rock to spring open and reveal its câche.

Nevertheless, as with other spring flowers such as daffodils and bluebells, rural Devonians still consider it unlucky to take a small bunch of primroses into the house of a poultry farmer, because the number of chickens, goslings or ducklings reared that season is supposed to be equivalent to the numbers of primroses in the bunch. Sarah Hewitt, who reported the superstition in 'Nummits and Crummits', stated that she had once seen a small girl severely punished in South Devon for committing this offence.

Medicinally, primroses have been used locally in the treatment of chapped skin: the flowers and smaller leaves were boiled in best lard and the preparation rubbed into the sore areas.

Mixed with the juice of sage, primrose juice was considered to be an excellent method of restoring the voice in cases of laryngitis. And primrose leaves, eaten raw, are still recommended for sufferers from arthritis.

QUINCE *(Chaenomeles japonica)*

– Squinch

Though unpleasantly hard and tart when raw, the golden, apple-like fruits of this shrub have long been used by country-folk to make delicious jellies and wines. A local superstition, dating back to the seventeenth century maintains that if a pregnant woman eats abundantly of the quince, the children she bears will be blessed with wisdom and intelligence. Certainly, this plant has a long history of medicinal usage. In Chudleigh it was considered to be a good remedy for a running-nose. Quince kernels were heated in new milk until this had almost reached the boil, and the mixture was then left until it was cool enough to be snuffed up the nose, 4 or 5 times a day.

Quince seeds are still considered to be effective in the treatment of diarrhoea. A farmer's wife from South Devon saves the seeds when the fruits have ripened; an ounce should be placed in a pan of cold water and brought slowly to the boil, then removed from the heat and allowed to stand until cold. The brew should be strained and given to the patient in the dose of a dessertspoonful for a child and a wineglassful for an adult.

From the same source comes the information that whole ripe quinces may be boiled in a very little water until a jelly-like consistency is reached. This gel, when massaged into the scalp and hair, acts as an excellent hair conditioner.

RASPBERRY (*Rubus idaeus*)

Although raspberries can occasionally be seen growing wild on certain heaths they are more commonly found in the fruit garden.

The raspberry has been used medicinally for many years. It is perhaps best known for the benefits it brings to pregnant women, for the plant is an effective muscle relaxant. Hence, it has been found that an infusion of the leaves, drunk regularly during the last three months of pregnancy, results in an easy and relatively painless labour. The same treatment has also brought relief to women who suffer from painful periods.

In South Devon consumptive patients used to be given an infusion made from raspberry leaves, agrimony and barberry bark.

At the beginning of the nineteenth century in North Devon, raspberry jam was highly thought of in the treatment of 'the stone and gravel': a dessertspoonful was to be taken once a day in a glass of gin and water.

ROSE (*Rosa spp.*)

– Canker Bell/Berry
– Cat-hip
– Ewe Bramble/Brimble
– Hep
– Hook-Brimble
– Pig's Noses – Dog Rose (Rosa canina)
– Pig's Rose
– Pixy-Pear
– Yew Brimmel
– Yoe Brimble
– Soldiers

– Apothecary's Rose – Red Rose (Rosa gallica)

The old-fashioned, sweet-smelling rose has an ancient history. Originally dedicated to Venus, the Roman goddess of love, it came to be adopted by Christians as a symbol of the Blessed Virgin, and the earliest Rosaries consisted of strings of 'beads' made from pressed petals. A single rose came to be regarded as the emblem of perfection, and was soon associated with Christian ideals such as martyrdom, virginity, and divine love.

The association between roses and love has endured in Devonian folklore, which maintains that anyone who dreams of picking this flower will have good luck and happiness in love. Young girls in the county used it to learn the identity of their future husbands: they were instructed to pick the rose on Midsummer's Day, then to pack it away carefully and leave it undisturbed until Christmas. If worn to Church on Christmas Day their future lover would come and take it from them. Robert Herrick seems to have known of this custom, for he says of a bride:

'She must no more a-Maying,
Or, by Rosebuds divine
Who'll be her valentine.'

Roses also had their ceremonial uses in Devon. It used to be traditional to strew rose-petals along the bridal path, a custom again referred to by Herrick in these lines from the 'Hesperides':

'The showers of roses, lucky foure-leav'd grasse,
The while the cloud of youngling sing
And drown ye with a flowrie spring.'

The same flower had its place in the funeral service, for while red roses were usually planted on the grave of a virgin, white roses were placed on that of someone who was considered to have led a truly good life. This association probably accounts for the local superstition concerning the 'death-rose', one having green sepals mixed with the petals, which was considered to be a portent of death. And for Robert Herrick, all roses served as a reminder of the transience of life, as these lines betray:

'Gather ye rosebuds while ye may,
Old Time is still a-flying.
And this same flower that smiles today,
Tomorrow will be dying.'

Roses also have their medicinal uses, and rose hips – known locally as Pigs' noses or pixy-pears – are considered one of the highest sources of Vitamin C, a syrup made from them traditionally being given to babies. To make rose hip syrup the hips should be gathered from the wild dog rose when they are ripe but before they become too soft. The heads and stalks are removed from the fruit, which is then split in half so that the seeds and white pith may be removed and discarded. Having been sieved or blended, the fruit is weighed and equal weights of sugar and water added. The mixture is then brought slowly to the boil and simmered until soft and syrupy – it should be stirred continuously during this stage. The resultant syrup may now be strained and put into bottles with close-fitting lids, ready for use. Once opened, the syrup should be stored in a refrigerator and used quite quickly.

ROSEMARY

(Rosemarinus officinalis)

The uses of rosemary in Devon have been many and varied: valued for its medicinal and cosmetic benefits, the protective powers which it was supposed to possess led to its being included among Christmas decorations, wedding flowers or funeral herbs. Herrick wrote:

'Grow it for two ends, it matters not at all,
Be't for my bridall, or my buriall.'

Rosemary has traditionally been included in the bouquet of a Devon bride because it was believed to bring good luck and fertility to the happy couple. Its talisman properties are still recognised, for a resident of Stockleigh Pomeroy recently asserted that the

planting of a rosemary bush near a cottage would ensure that no witch could ever harm its occupants.

The emblem of remembrance, this plant was one of the chief funeral herbs. Sprigs of rosemary were distributed to mourners and thrown into the grave as the coffin was being lowered into it; rosemary bushes were frequently planted on graves.

The cosmetic qualities of this herb have long been recognised. In Barnstaple at the beginning of the century it was used as a means of preventing baldness since it is generally believed to possess the ability to stimulate hair growth. Generous quantities of rosemary were boiled in water that had been gathered from the hollows at the feet of huge beech trees, and the decoction used to bathe the scalp. As early as the seventeenth century rosemary flowers were boiled in white wine and the mixture drunk to sweeten the breath; the same mixture could also be used to wash the face, for it was said to be highly beneficial to the complexion, or alternatively to treat dandruff.

Medicinally, owing to its bitterness the plant has been valued as a tonic, and rosemary tea is still recommended for convalescent patients, as well as for those wishing to improve their memories. And before 1700 Lady Clifford of Ugbrooke House, near Chudleigh, used the herb to treat ear complaints and headaches. For deafness she recommended that one should:

> *'Boil a good quantity of Rosemary flowers in Rosewater, then milk some breast milk upon it, lay it upon wool, and apply as hot as can be borne to the ears morning and evening for 2 - 3 days.'*

For a headache, however, one should:

> *'Mix 2sp. each of Rosemary, Camomile juice, Woman's milk and Wine vinegar over a low heat, then steep in it a piece of dried Rose cake; when this has absorbed the liquor and is thoroughly hot, strew in 2 grated nutmegs and break the Rose cake in two, binding one half to each temple, and so let the party lay down to rest.'*

A rather more modern treatment for headache from South Devon calls for the leaves and small side-shoots of rosemary to be infused in a pint of water, and a wineglass of the infusion to be taken whenever relief from a headache is needed.

RUE *(Ruta graveolens)*

– Herb of grace

The word rue means 'repentance', and as this state of mind is necessary to obtain the grace of God, the plant has become known as the 'Herb of Grace'. In the Middle Ages it was highly valued by the Church, whose priests considered it to be powerful against all forms of evil and hence made use of it when conducting exorcisms. Devon brides have traditionally included the herb in their bridal bouquet to ensure that the union would be blessed with fortune and happiness and protected from malevolent influences, and country people believed that rubbing the floor of their houses with rue would prevent witches from entering.

The belief that rue could drive away evil or disease is reflected in its official name 'Ruta', said to come from a Greek word meaning 'to drive away': 'graveolens', is derived from two Latin words – 'gravis' (heavy) and 'oleo' (smell) – and refers to the plant's potent aroma. This aroma is repugnant to some creatures, and Devon housewives were quick to take advantage of the fact, for they found that rubbing rue over meat would ensure that no flies would settle upon it.

The combination of protective powers and strong scent led to rue being adopted as an early form of disinfectant at times when infectious disease was prevalent. It was strewn, for example, in Assize Courts and worn by officials to ward off 'jail-fever'.

Rue was one of the ingredients in an Antidote to the Fever which appeared in Trueman's Exeter Paper on 12th March, 1808:-

> *'Take of the essential oils of Rue, Rosemary and Wormwood each a drachm; dilute them with about ½ tablespoon of spirits of wine. Infuse in an earthern pot (over a moderate heat) a handful of Sage in a quart of distilled vinegar, till the vinegar has extracted a good deal of strength from the sage. Strain it through a flannel, and add the diluted oils, then dissolve ¼ oz. camphor in 1½ ozs spirits of wine – care must be taken in mixing this; it must be added a little at a time, shaking it well each time. It must be shaken before it is used.*
>
> *With this, wash the face, loins and mouth, and on approaching infected persons or places smell a sponge dipped in it; wear also a little camphor in a bag near the stomach.'*

And together with sage and either briar or elder, rue was useful in the seventeenth century for counteracting the Plague: the ingredients were pounded together (a handful of each), strained with a quart of white wine, and mixed with a little ginger and a spoonful of treacle. This was then drunk morning and evening.

From the same period, a cure for deafness found in the records of Ugbrooke House, near Chudleigh, recommends that a little Rue be taken in the fingers and fashioned into a long roll; this should then be dipped in salad oil and inserted into the ears every 10 hours. The cure probably worked by softening and dispersing any wax which had accumulated in the ears.

For those wishing to plant rue in their gardens, Lady Rosalind Northcote relates in her 'Book of Herbs' that the herb thrives much better if it has been stolen!

RUSHES

(Juncus spp.)

To the country-dwellers of the past, rushes were important plants which were put to a variety of uses about the house. The stiff stems could be woven together to make baskets or matting, and the pith contained within them used to make rush-lights. For this purpose, the rushes were picked when they were full-grown, but still green. Most of the outer covering was carefully peeled away, only a tiny part being left throughout the 20-60 cm length in order to lend some support to the exposed pith: this was then dipped into lard or tallow, drained and left to cool. Once set, the light was ready to be burnt.

Rushes also feature in a number of Devonian charms. One, which dates from the 1920s and was reported from Hartland, advises a sufferer from warts to pick 3 rushes, rub them over the warts, and then tie them together and throw them away. In this rather anti-social cure it seems that the warts will be transferred to the unfortunate person who unsuspectingly picks up the discarded bundle!

Fifty years earlier than this, rushes were used in Hatherleigh in a charm for 'girding' (shingles). This required that the sufferer be taken in the morning to 'running-water', where his attendant should pick 7 rushes growing near, but not in, the stream. These were then to be laid directly upon the affected skin, and drawn across it: they should next be thrown into the stream, on the principle that as they were washed away, the disease would be washed away with them. This charm required that the treatment be repeated with fresh rushes for three mornings in succession.

The Hatherleigh cure is only one example of the way in which rushes were used to treat cases of shingles. A white witch from North Devon used to twine them together to form a wreath or ring, which he would place over the affected area, and then hang inside his chimney. Once again, the process had to be repeated on three successive occasions.

At Merton, the procedure was more complicated. First, a bullrush – female for a male patient and male for a female – had to be procured and then drawn around the body by the right side, care having been taken to ensure that the patient was turned towards the sun. Once the bullrush had encircled the body, it had to be tied in a knot, and when it was burnt some time later the malady was supposed to die with it. Next, it was necessary for a woman to pluck some wool from a ram, make it into a bandage, and lay it upon the afflicted part: this remained in position for 2-3 days and was subsequently burnt. Finally, the patient was dosed with a medicine to purify the blood, and any sore area bathed with olive oil.

SAGE *(Salvia officinalis)*

Sage is a herb which is said to be in sympathy with its owners: a very old superstition maintains that it will fade with the fortunes of the house, and revive only when they recover. The people of Plymouth saw a flourishing sage-bush as a sign that the mistress was head of the house-hold, and in Bishop's Nympton it used to be the custom after a wedding for the bride and groom each to plant a small bush of sage – whoever's grew the largest would rule the roost! The plant was also believed to be an aphrodisiac.

Medicinally, sage has the reputation of being very good for sore-throats. It should be boiled in water, and the strained liquid used as a gargle: the leaves may also be made into a poultice and laid upon the chest. Of the four known varieties of sage, red sage is considered the most effective in such instances. And a seventeenth century South Devon cure deems the juices of sage and primrose, when swallowed, to be a speedy means of restoring the voice of anyone suffering from laryngitis.

Sage is still used today as a hair tonic: the herb is boiled in water and the decoction used as a final rinse. Alternatively, the same brew may be used to bathe the head of anyone suffering from a headache, or to soothe sunburnt skin.

Sage tea is thought to be beneficial to anyone suffering from shingles. The leaves, when chewed, are also said to prevent toothache and to whiten the teeth.

SCARLET PIMPERNEL
(Anagallis arvenis)

– Father's Weatherglass
– Grandfather's Weatherglass
– Little Jane
– Shepherd's Calendar
– Shepherd's Sundial
– Urith's Blood

The sprawling scarlet-pimpernel is a common weed of waste and cultivated land, roadsides and sand dunes. It is often known as 'Father's weatherglass', because country-folk became aware that if it opened out in the morning fine weather might be expected, whilst rain would follow if its petals remained tight shut. Additionally, the scarlet-pimpernel keeps regular hours, opening at around 8 am and shutting for the day in mid-afternoon: from this it has also become known as 'Shepherd's Sundial', for farmers used it to tell the time of day.

Indeed, this little flower has quite a reputation in Devon: one rhyme says of it:-

'No ear hath heard, no tongue can tell
The virtues of the pimpernel.'

One of these virtues, according to the people of Tavistock, was the power to charm away warts. Nine scarlet pimpernel flowers were placed in a silk bag together with nine leaves of heart fever grass, and this was then worn around the neck. Then, night and morning, the bag was held over the warts and this rhyme recited:-

'Herb Pimpernel, I have thee found
Growing on Christ Jesus ground
The same gift, Lord Jesu have thee
When His blood He shed to spare thee.
Herb grass this evil pass,
And God bless all who wear thee.
Amen.'

The verse was a vital part of the charm, which was said to be ineffective without it.

SEA HOLLY *(Eryngium maritimum)*

As its name suggests, Sea-Holly is a plant which grows on sandy and shingly shores around our coasts. At first sight it resembles a thistle, for it is stiff and prickly. Its quite large spiny leaves are deeply toothed and blue-green, with a dull bloom over their surface. The tiny blue flowers appear between July and September, and are clustered together into dense round heads which, like the leaf bracts at their base, are extremely prickly.

There is a very curious and ancient belief concerning goats and sea-holly, for it is said that if a goat bites off a piece of this plant it will cause her to stand quite still, and the whole of

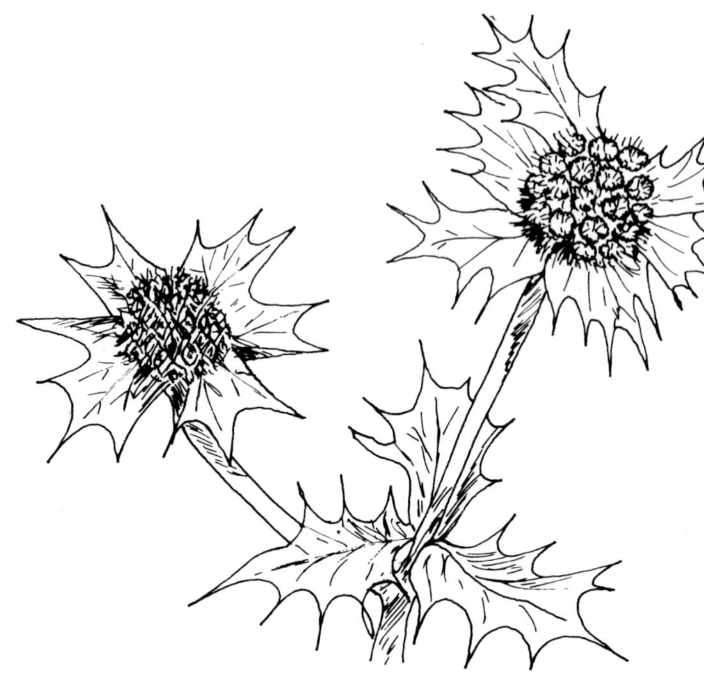

the rest of the herd with her. The spell will continue until someone takes the piece of plant out of the goat's mouth!

SOUTHERNWOOD
(Artemesia arbrotanum)

- Boy's Love
- Kiss-me-quick-and-go
- Lad's Love
- Maiden's Ruin
- Old Man

Southernwood is a shrub grown mainly in sunny, sheltered garden borders. It reaches a height of about 1 metre, and has a woody stem and delicate, grey-green, feathery leaves which have a rich lemon-scent when crushed. Although the plant can produce tiny yellow flowers, the climate of Devon is rarely warm enough to allow them to form.

The inhabitants of South Molton have traditionally been wary of growing Southernwood in their gardens, for they believed it to be a plant which attracts sickness. A local woman decided to pay a call on a neighbour who was lying ill in her lonely cottage. Walking up the drive, she noticed a considerable quantity of southernwood flourishing in the flower beds, uprooted it, and the patient quickly recovered!

There is an old Devon rhyme which links two local names for this plant, maintaining that:-

" 'Boy's Love' is 'Maiden's Ruin'
But half of it is her own doing."

Perhaps behind this saying lies the belief, again reported from South Molton, that Southernwood may be made into an infusion and drunk to prevent pregnancy.

The herb had other uses, too, for it was frequently hung in wardrobes. As well as repelling moths, it imparted its pleasant scent – strangely reminiscent of both lemon and lavender – to the clothes which were stored around it.

Medicinally, southernwood tea is still regarded as a good means of expelling intestinal worms: an ounce of the herb, either fresh or dried, should be scalded with a pint of boiling water and allowed to infuse for ten minutes. The recommended dose is a wineglassful to be taken morning and night for as long as necessary.

This plant was one of the principal ingredients of a salve, made by a well-known ointment-maker in Exeter up to her death at the beginning of the century. The salve was composed of southernwood, plantain leaves, blackcurrant leaves, elder buds, angelica and parsley, chopped, pounded and simmered with clarified butter (butter being highly esteemed because 'cows feed on herbs and all herbs are good for something'). This ointment was very highly thought of locally in the treatment of burns and rawness of the skin.

SPEEDWELL *(Veronica spp.)*

– Angel's eyes
– Bird's eye (Bow, Northam)
– Blue bird's eye – (V. chamaedrys)
– Break-your-mother's-heart

The commonest type of speedwell in Devon is the germander speedwell, an attractive bright blue flower that grows on hedgebanks and grassy verges, along paths and field edges, in woods and on cultivated land.

Several reasons have been given to explain why this plant has been named the 'speedwell'. Some claim that the petals, which fall almost as soon as the flower is picked, suggest a parting, so the name is really a farewell – 'speed you well'. It seems to have been customary in past times to pin sprays of speedwell onto the clothing of travellers, for this was supposed to preserve them in good health and fortune during their journey.

Alternatively, the name 'speedwell' could also reflect the high regard felt for its medicinal powers: the old country herbalists used it to treat a wide range of complaints, from simple coughs to tuberculosis, and from fleshy wounds to leprosy.

However, local superstition has also endowed the flower with the ability to cause illness. Schoolchildren in Bow and Northam at the turn of the century were told that if they picked speedwell they would fall ill with the unpleasant disease known as 'The King's Evil' (Scrophula). In addition, since the flower, through its blue, eye-like appearance was widely known as 'bird's eye', it was rumoured that anyone who destroyed it would have his eyes pecked out by a vengeful robin!

In some parts, the speedwell is also known as 'break-your-mother's-heart', a curious name given to it because its fruit is heart-shaped.

All speedwells belong to the genus 'Veronica': some authorities claim that the name is derived from two Greek words meaning 'I bring victory', and refers to the successful cures thought to have been wrought by this little herb. Christians, however, may prefer to think that the genus was dedicated to St. Veronica, the compassionate woman who is believed to have wiped Christ's face as he carried the cross to the summit of Calvary.

The germander speedwell is one of nature's weather-forecasters, for it closes its petals before rain, and only opens them again when it ceases.

ST. JOHN'S WORT

(Hypericum spp.)

– Devil's Flight
– Rose of Sharon (Hartland)
– Star of Bethlehem

This golden-yellow flower was named after John the Baptist, for it was believed that it came into bloom on his feast day, 24th June. The red sap in the stems, leaves and flowers was held to represent the blood of the martyr.

The St. John's Wort was considered in Devon to be a plant with strong magical powers; its juice, combined with those of dill and vervain and used to anoint the eyes for three days running, was said to enable the spirits of the air to become visible to mortal man. The leaves and flowers of the plant, if culled on St. John's Day or on a Friday, then dried and hung in a jar by the window, were believed to offer protection against evil spirits, fire or thunderbolts. Alternatively, they could be worn around the neck as a love charm, or to prevent mental illness.

On the principle of the Doctrine of Signatures, since the leaves of St. John's Wort appear to be pitted with tiny holes like the pores of a man's skin, the plant was often used in the treatment of skin cuts or grazes. Flowers and leaves were mixed with olive-oil and found to have an antiseptic effect when applied to such wounds, and also to bed-sores.

An infusion of St. John's Wort was also given to relieve coughing, or to prevent bed-wetting.

THISTLE *(Carduus spp.)*

– Dappled Thistle – Milk Thistle – Thistlefinch – Milky Dashle – Lady's Thistle	– Carduus (Silybus) marianus
– Blessed Thistle – Holy Thistle	– Carduus benedictus

Although there are many types of thistle, no-one who has ever inadvertantly sat down upon one of them, or stepped on it with bare feet, will ever forget that the leaves, and sometimes the stems also, are covered in sharp spines. One of the best-known varieties is the lilac-coloured cotton-thistle (Onopordon acanthium) for this is the heraldic emblem of Scotland. The yellow carline thistle is also familiar, for when dried it is frequently included in flower-arrangements. In Devon, however, it is the milk thistle and the blessed thistle which feature most frequently in local herbal lore.

The milk thistle is so called because of the legend that the Virgin Mary spilt milk upon it whilst nursing the Infant Jesus, and thus caused it to remain dappled ever after, hence such local names as 'milky dashle' or 'lady's thistle'. People in Devon still believe that if a lactating mother takes this plant, it will cause her flow of milk to increase.

'Thistlefinch' is another popular name for the milk thistle, and refers to the fact the goldfinches feed upon its seeds. However, birds were not alone in finding it good to eat, for country folk in the past used it as a type of 'greens': the young and tender stalks of the root leaves were stripped of their spines and boiled, and if taken in spring were believed to purify the blood of winter ills. Because of its prickly nature, the milk thistle was considered to be an effective cure for a stitch in the side – a good example of the Doctrine of Signatures, whereby plants were believed to bear some indication of the purpose for which they were intended.

The blessed thistle was also used medicinally, in cases of hysteria and depression. A tea made from it, and taken several times a day, was said to be highly beneficial.

This same flower was used by young girls in the past to reveal which of their suitors loved them best: they would take one thistle for each lover, and give each the name of a suitor. Then the heads would be cut off, and the thistles placed under the pillow. The first to sprout would reveal the truest love.

For those troubled with unwelcome thistles on their land, the advice from South Molton is:-

'Cut them in June, cut them too soon;
Cut them in July, they are sure to die.'

But this is contradicted by another saying which warns:-

"Cut your thistles before St. John (24th June)
Or you'll have two instead of one.'

TRAVELLER'S JOY

(Clematis vitalba)

- Aaron's Beard
- Boys' Bacca
- Bushy-beard
- Daddy's whiskers
- Devil's cut
- Goat's Beard
- Old Man's Beard
- Smoking cane

Travellers' Joy smothers hedgerows and the edges of woodland throughout the county, its stems reaching over 30m. in length. The plant climbs by means of its leaf-stalks which twine themselves around nearby shrubs. Like its garden cousins, this clematis has no petals, its flowers – which are evident in July and August – being composed of very pale green, turned-back sepals, topped by domes of long stamens.

The fruits of traveller's joy – so called because of the pleasure the plant gave to wayfarers wandering the hedgerows of the countryside – develop in the autumn and are very conspicuous, since long feathery styles issue from them in whisker-like fashion. It is for this reason that the plant has been given such names as 'goat's beard' and 'daddy's whiskers'.

Two more popular names for traveller's joy are 'boy's bacca', and 'smoking cane', and they betray one use to which it was put in former times, for young boys used to smoke the dried stems. Unless these stems really are dry and dead, however, they contain an irritant sap which can raise ulcers on any part of the skin which it touches. Illicit smokers may have learnt of this to their cost, but beggars made the most of it, for by applying fresh twigs to their limbs they could cause unsightly blisters to appear upon them. These aroused public sympathy and the beggar found that his income rose accordingly!

VERVAIN *(Verbena officinalis)*

– Wizard's herb

Throughout history Vervain has been associated with magic, as its popular name of 'Wizard's herb' suggests. It was one of the plants traditionally said to have been used by witches in casting their spells, and Devonian folklore maintains that if one combines the juices of vervain, dill and St. John's Wort, and uses the mixture to anoint the eyes for three days in succession, then one will be able to perceive the spirits of the air.

The Druids valued Vervain highly, including it in all their magic potions, and its Latin name – Verbena – hints at an older history still, for this was a term used by the Romans to describe plants which decorated sacrificial altars. Additionally, vervain is said to have been the only plant considered fitting to sweep the Altar of Jupiter, the King of the Gods.

Like dill, vervain was believed to have the power of overcoming evil forces, so as well as being used by witches, it was also thought to protect against them. There is a local saying which asserts that:

'Vervain and Dill
Hinder witches from their will.'

According to popular superstition, calamity and infection could also be averted through this plant. It was thought to ward off the plague, and was frequently worn around the neck as a talisman against headaches and poisonous bites. Its very name reflects its supposed ability to banish all forms of evil, for it is derived from a Celtic word meaning 'to drive away'. An infusion made from its roots was said to put to flight all manner of illness, ridding victims of such varied complaints as jaundice, dysentry, dropsy, fevers and diseases of the ear, nose and throat. It was held to be good for eye conditions, too, since doves and pigeons were believed to cure their own dimness of vision by eating it.

The healing powers of vervain were considered to be at their most potent when treating injuries caused upon the battlefield. It was said that the plant could confer immortality upon heroes, and heal all wounds received in war: it was thus able to recognise and reward valour. This property was saluted by Christian legend also, for this claimed that vervain grew on Mount Calvary at the time of the crucifixion, and was used to staunch the bleeding from Christ's wounds. In commemoration of this, it is customary to bless the flower as one picks it.

WALLFLOWER

(Cheiranthus cheiri)

- Crucifix-flower
- Warrior
- Bleeding Heart
- Bliddy waryers
- Bloody Warrior
- Gillyflower
- Jellyflower

Today the wallflower is most commonly found cultivated in our gardens, but it occasionally escapes to brighten old walls and hedgebanks. The romantic legend of how it came into being is related by Robert Herrick in this poem from the 'Hesperides':

'Why this flower is now called so,
List sweet maids and you shall know.
Understand this firstling was
Once a brisk and bonny lass,
Kept as close as Danae was:
Who a sprightly springall loved,
And to have it fully proved,
Up she got upon a wall,
Tempting down to slide withall:
But the silken twist untied,
So she fell, and bruised, she died.
Love, in pity of the deed,
And her loving-luckless speed,
Turned her to this plant, we call
Now the Flower of the Wall'.

The memory of this legend persists in a children's game which was still played in Clovelly a decade ago. The players form a circle, and one stands towards the wall. All then sing:

'Wallflower, wallflower, growing up so high
This young lady is sure to die.
Turn your face towards the wall
And tell me what your sweetheart's called'.

Whereupon the player facing the wall calls out a name, and all chase round a good-sized plot of land and kiss. The game then starts all over again with the next person standing towards the wall.

This attractive flower has long been regarded as a symbol of fidelity, and some claim that such local names as 'warrior' and 'bloody warrior' refer to an ancient practice whereby soldiers used to wear a sprig of wallflower as a sign of constancy to their sweethearts back home.

WILD CELERY

(Apium graveolens)

– Celery-grist
– Smallage
– Water Parsley

Wild Celery has been widely used in the past in the treatment of skin complaints. In the seventeenth century it was thought to heal boils (known locally as 'fellon', 'pinsoles' or 'blackheads'): a good handful of smallage was pounded and mixed with a new-laid egg, a spoonful of honey and a handful of wheat or bean flour. This was then applied twice daily.

Wild Celery has also been found effective in the healing of burns. An Exeter gentleman witnessed the following cure just after the end of the First World War: his sister, who was about 15 at the time, was very badly burnt at the back of her head and shoulders, and the local doctor felt himself powerless to help. An old herbalist living nearby heard about the accident and claimed to be able to heal the child: he gathered wild celery and boiled it in water, and then used the liquor to bathe the burns. He subsequently applied the wild celery as a plaster. The treatment proved to be effective, and is said to be equally useful for healing infected breasts.

Smallage could be taken internally as well, and was one of the ingredients of an early 'cure' for scurvy, to be undergone twice a year in the Spring and Autumn. Two handfuls each of scurvy-grass, watercress, brooklime, red sage, smallage and rue were pounded together to extract the juice: this was then added to 2 quarts of white wine, and 9 spoonfuls drunk in the morning before food, and again at teatime 'till it be all done'.

WOOD SORREL

(Oxalis acetosella)

– Bird's Bread and Cheese
– Cuckoo's Bread and Cheese
– Fairy Bells
– God Almighty's Bread and Cheese
– Green Sauce
– Rabbits' Meat
– Rabbits' Flowers
– Shamrock
– Sour Grab
– Sour Sap
– Stubwort

A plant of woods and hedgebanks, wood sorrel flourishes in shady areas. Its dainty white or pink petals, finely veined with purple, are apparent between April and August nodding from stalks some 5-15 cm. long. The leaves and stems have a sharp, acid taste, which explains such local names as 'sour grab' and 'sour sauce'.

Like the scarlet-pimpernel, wood sorrel can be used to forecast the weather, for it too opens its flowers in anticipation of sunshine and closes them when rain is on its way. The leaves are also significant, for they fold down upon themselves at night or in dull conditions.

Residents of Newton Abbot have used this plant to soothe and heal bruises; the sorrel should be boiled, allowed to cool slightly, and applied to the bruised area. The water in which it has been boiled may also be used to bathe the injury. The plant is in fact known locally as 'stubwort', and was useful for treating animals as well as humans. An old remedy states that 'stubwort, lapped in red dock leafe and roasted in hot cinders, will eat away the dead flesh in a horse's sore.

WORMWOOD

(Artemesia absinthium)

- Wil Wormuth
- Wormeth
- Wormuth

Wormwood has a very long tradition of being a powerful herb against witches, and was supposed to be particularly effective in guarding against evil spirits. On a more practical level, it was also thought to be an excellent means of keeping a house free of parasites, as this old country rhyme asserts:-

'Where the chamber is swept and wormwood thrown,
No flea for his life dare bide to be known'.

Medicinally, the herb was used in the seventeenth century in South Devon to treat cases of dropsy, or of rawness of the stomach: the juice was drunk at frequent intervals, as well as with all meals. In addition, raisins were stuffed with the plant and a few eaten in the morning before food.

From the same period, sufferers from flatulence might well have been treated with a remedy similar to that of Lady Clifford's 'wind water'. This called for:-

'a spoonful each of Wormwood, Spearmint and Cardamom;
½ lb Red Sage
1 oz each of Carraway seeds, Sweet Fennel seeds and Aniseed.'

The herbs were shredded and the seeds broken up, and the mixture then steeped in 3 quarts of sack (a dry, warmed, and often spiced sherry) for two days and nights. The result was distilled and sweetened with a little sugar, and a glassful given to the patient.

This herb could also be used in place of camomile to cure a stitch in the side: a wooden dish was filled with alternating layers of wormwood and hot embers, and a linen cloth fixed over it. The dish was then held, as hot as could be borne, against the side of the body.

As its name suggests, wormwood was formerly given to children suffering from worms: a handful each of wormwood, rue, feverfew and unset leeks were boiled together with a little mother-thyme in a pint of white wine vinegar until half evaporated. The mixture was then strained and the herbs placed in a small linen bag which was laid, as hot as the child could bear it, between the navel and stomach. The bag was placed there for three nights, having first been warmed in the strained vinegar.

Anyone tempted to experiment with wormwood, however, should do so with extreme caution. The above remedy wisely calls only for external application of the herb, for although it has been found that wormwood does indeed contain a substance – santonin – which dispels worms, this can cause quite severe hallucinations if taken in excess. It seems that too much wormwood can also damage the heart.

YARROW *(Achillea millefolium)*

– Carpenter's weed
– Soldiers' woundwort

Yarrow was one of the plants which young girls in Devon used 'to see a lover in a dream'. The yarrow had to be plucked from the grave of a young man, and the following rhyme recited:

> *'Yarrow, sweet yarrow, the first that I have found,*
> *And in the name of Jesus I pluck it from the ground.*
> *As Joseph loved sweet Mary and took her for his dear,*
> *So in a dream this night, I hope my true love will appear.'*

If the yarrow was then placed under the pillow, the future love would appear in a dream that night.

The name 'yarrow' is said to be a corruption of the Greek word 'hiera', meaning 'holy herb'. Perhaps this explains the old custom whereby a spray of yarrow was often hung inside a baby's cradle. It was believed that its presence would ensure that the child remained happy and contented.

This plant has a long history of medicinal use. One of its old names is 'soldiers' woundwort', supposedly because it was formerly used to heal wounds on the battlefield. Its generic name 'Achillea' is in fact said to commemorate the fact that the great Achilles himself used yarrow leaves to treat his injured warriors.

Carpenters, too, respected the healing powers of yarrow and often made use of it when they hurt themselves during the course of their work – hence its other local name of 'carpenters' weed'.

Yarrow leaves are also said to be excellent for head-colds and catarrh: an ounce hould be infused in a pint of boiling water for ten minutes, and the infusion then strained and bottled. A wineglassful taken night and morning is supposed to give prompt relief.

YEW *(Taxus baccata)*

Yew trees have a very long life-span, and so have become symbolic of ever-lasting life. This is why mourners used to lay sprays of yew in the graves of departed loved-ones, and why at one time sprigs of it were placed inside shrouds before they were sewn up. Robert Herrick referred to such customs in his poem 'To the Yew and Cypress to grace his Funeral':

'Both you two have
Relation to the grave:
And where
The Fun'rall-Trump sounds, you are there.

I shall be made
Ere long a fleeting shade:
Pray come,
And do some honour to my tomb.

Do not deny
My last request, for I
Will be
Thankful to you, or friends, for me.'

The yew signified that life was not totally extinct, but rather that it would continue in the Resurrection to come. As such a symbol of the triumph of life over death, it naturally became included by the church among its Easter decorations.

In view of these associations, it was usual to plant yews in churchyards. Devonians have always considered it extremely unlucky to cut down a churchyard Yew, or to damage its branches in any way. Neither would they burn yew wood, or take it indoors. Generally yew trees are treated with respect in the county: there is an ancient one at Stoke Gabriel which is believed to have the power to grant the wishes of anyone who walks around it seven times backwards. Local residents value this tree so highly that in April 1969 they caused 38 new props to be erected to support its ancient branches.

An old Devonian interpretation maintains that to dream of yew-trees indicates that one will soon hear of the death of an elderly person in whom one has a vested interest.